HOLT
ENVIRONMENT SCIENCE

LABORATORY GUIDE

HOLT, RINEHART AND WINSTON
Harcourt Brace & Company
Austin • New York • Orlando • Atlanta • San Francisco • Boston • Dallas • Toronto • London

CONTRIBUTORS

WRITERS

Robert Avakian
Trinity School
Midland, Texas

Kimberly Berg
Salado High School
Salado, Texas

Rainy Day
Geographer
Austin, Texas

Lynn Diebolt-Lewis
Olivet High School
Olivet, Michigan

Patricia Doran
Rondout Valley
    Jr. High School
Accord, New York

Jim Dunlap
Living Materials Center
Plano Independent School
    District
Plano, Texas

Richard Filson
Edison High School
Stockton, California

Claudia Fowler
University Laboratory School
Baton Rouge, Louisiana

Natalie Goldstein
Ithaca, New York

Stephanie Lanoue
Lago Vista High School
Lago Vista, Texas

Michael Lubich
Mapletown High School
Greensboro, Pennsylvania

Wendy Lym
Science Writer
Denver, Colorado

Patricia Merkord
Austin High School
Austin, Texas

Alyson Mike
Radley Middle School
Helena, Montana

Bruce Mulkey
Austin, Texas

Gabriell DeBear Paye
West Roxbury High School
Jamaica Plain, Massachusetts

Carol Quay
Heritage Conservancy
Doylestown, Pennsylvania

William M. Quay
Radnor School District
Wayne, Pennsylvania

Marie Ratliff
Austin, Texas

Sandra Tauer
Derby Middle School
Derby, Kansas

Carol Wagner
Pflugerville High School
Pflugerville, Texas

Ruth Willey
Fremont Ross High School
Fremont, Ohio

REVIEWERS

Margaret A. Brumsted
Dartmouth High School
Dartmouth, Massachusetts

Lynette Celano
St. Gregory Catholic School
Phoenix, Arizona

Anthony Eagan
Cajon High School
San Bernadino, California

Joseph Fontaine
Ecologist
Tehachapi, California

Susan Haskew
Texas Natural Resource
    Conservation Commission
Austin, Texas

Janis Lariviere
Westlake High School
Alternative Learning Center
Austin, Texas

Sheila Lightbourne
Choctawhatchee
    High School
Fort Walton Beach, Florida

Barbara Pietrucha
Neptune Middle School
Neptune, New Jersey

Marie Rediess
Algonac High School
Algonac, Michigan

Denice Sandefur
Nucla High School
Nucla, Colorado

Eva Silverfine, M.Sc.
Ecologist
San Marcos, Texas

Mark Stallings
Gilmer High School
Ellijay, Georgia

John M. Trimble
Corona Del Sol High School
Tempe, Arizona

Carol Wagner
Pflugerville High School
Pflugerville, Texas

Paul W. Wilson
Owasso High School
Owasso, Oklahoma

Photography Credits
Front Cover: water testing, Tom Stewart/The Stock Market; erosion, Carr Clifton/Minden Pictures; Ganges delta, World Perspectives/Tony Sone Images; ferns; Pat O'Hara/Tony Stone Images; cheetah, Jeff Hunter/Image Bank; clouds, Robert Stahl/Tony Stone Images; windmills, Lester Lefkowitz/The Stock Market; lungs, Photo Researchers, Inc.; contour plowing, D. Wigget/Natural Selection; sunflower, Jim Brandenburg/Minden Pictures; highways, Jose Fuste Raga/The Stock Market

Back Cover:
Pat O'Hara/Tony Stone Images

Title Page:
Jim Brandenburg/Minden Pictures

Art Credits
All art, unless otherwise noted, by Holt, Rinehart & Winston
Page 7, Thomas Kennedy; 8, Thomas Kennedy; 15, Thomas Kennedy; 16, Thomas Kennedy; 25, Leslie Kell; 28, Thomas Kennedy; 30, Thomas Kennedy; 42, Leslie Kell.

Printed in the United States of America

ISBN 0-03-053842-4

4 5 6 862 03 02 01

TO THE STUDENT

Welcome to the *Holt Environmental Science Laboratory Guide.* The following pages describe how to dissect owl pellets to reconstruct an owl's prey, how to make a model well that detects groundwater contaminated by surface pollution, how to project population growth trends in your community, and so much more. Investigations like these give you the opportunity to learn about environmental science by *doing* it. Whether you are interested in an environmental or scientific career, or you simply want to use your knowledge of environmental science to help protect the environment, doing the Investigations will help you meet your goal.

Some of the Investigations in this book are designed for you to do individually; others involve working as part of a team. Some require you to use specific experimental procedures, while others are open-ended. Most of the Laboratory Investigations will ask you to use scientific methods to answer a question or to investigate how something works. This variety of activities mirrors the richness and diversity of the field of environmental science.

Also notice the worksheets printed on pages 113–140. These worksheets accompany the Investigations in your *Holt Environmental Science* Pupil's Edition.

The Investigations in this book offer fascinating questions, tough challenges, and enjoyable explorations of your environment. It's time to get started!

LABORATORY GUIDE

CONTENTS

WORKSHEETS FOR
TEXTBOOK INVESTIGATIONS

ABOUT SAFETY

Laboratory experiments are great aids to learning environmental science. However, they can involve hazards. To protect yourself and ensure the safety of others, use the safety practices described below and on the following pages.

SAFETY SYMBOLS

The following safety symbols indicate particular hazards that you may encounter while performing Investigations. You should learn what each symbol means and what precautions you should take.

 Wear approved chemical safety goggles. Wear goggles when working with a chemical or solution, when heating substances, or when using any mechanical device.

 Wear a laboratory apron or laboratory coat. Wear a laboratory apron or coat to prevent chemicals or chemical solutions from contacting skin or street clothes.

 Wear gloves. Wear gloves when working with chemicals, stains, or wild (unknown) plants or animals.

 Sharp/pointed object. Use extreme care with all sharp instruments such as scalpels, sharp probes, and knives. Do not cut objects while holding them in your hand; always place them on a suitable work surface. Never use double-edged razors in the laboratory.

 Electrical hazard. To avoid electric shock, never use equipment with frayed cords. Tape electrical cords to work surfaces to ensure that equipment cannot fall from a table. Also, never use electrical equipment around water or with wet hands or clothing. When disconnecting an electrical cord from an outlet, grasp the plug rather than the cord.

 Dangerous chemical/poison. Always wear appropriate protective equipment, including eye goggles, gloves, and a laboratory apron, when working with hazardous chemicals. Never taste, touch, or smell any substance, and never bring it close to your eyes unless specifically instructed to do so by your teacher. Never return unused chemicals to their original containers. Do not mix any chemicals unless your teacher tells you to do so. Also, never pour water into a strong acid or base because this may produce heat and spattering. Instead, add the acid or base slowly to water. If you get any acid or base on your skin, flush the area with water and contact your teacher right away. Finally, report any chemical spill to your teacher immediately.

Flame/heat. Whenever possible, use a hot plate for heating rather than a laboratory burner. Use test-tube holders, tongs, or heavy gloves to handle hot items. Do not put your hands or face over any boiling liquid. When heating chemicals, be sure the containers are made of heat-proof glass. Also, never point a heated test tube or other container at anyone. Be sure to turn off a heat source when you are finished using it.

 Glassware. Inspect glassware before use; never use chipped or cracked glassware. Do not attempt to insert glass tubing into a rubber stopper without specific instructions from your teacher. Clean up broken glass by using tongs and a brush and dustpan. Discard the pieces in a container labeled "sharps."

 Plants. Do not ingest any plant part used in the laboratory, especially seeds. Do not rub any sap or plant juice on your skin, eyes, or mucous membranes. Wear disposable polyethylene gloves when handling any wild plant. Wash hands thoroughly after handling any plant part. Avoid the smoke of burning plants. Finally, do not pick wildflowers or other plants unless instructed to do so by your teacher.

 Live animals. Do not touch or approach any animal in the wild. Always get your teacher's permission before bringing any animal into the school building. Handle animals only as your teacher directs. Always treat animals carefully and with respect.

 Biohazard. Wear appropriate personal protection, including disposable neoprene gloves and other gear provided by your teacher. Clean your work area with disinfectant before you begin and after you complete the Investigation. Do not touch your face or rub your skin, eyes, or mucous membranes. Wash your hands thoroughly after use. Dispose of materials as instructed by your teacher.

LABORATORY SAFETY

When working in the laboratory, always follow the safety guidelines described in detail on pages 425–428 of your *Holt Environmental Science* textbook. Those safety guidelines are summarized here.

While in the laboratory, at all times . . .

be prepared. Read any Investigation thoroughly before attempting to do it. Know the locations of emergency equipment, and learn how to use it. Also, be sure that you know how to perform the emergency procedures for fire, chemical exposure, etc. that are found on pages 426–427 of your textbook.

stay organized. Keep your work area neat. Bring to class only books and other materials that are needed to conduct an Investigation.

do not proceed without supervision. Never perform any experiment that has not been specifically assigned by your teacher. And never work alone in the laboratory.

wear the right protective clothing. Wear close-toed shoes to protect your feet from accidental spills or dropped equipment. Tie back long hair, roll up loose sleeves, and put on any personal protective equipment required by your teacher.

watch for safety symbols. Be alert to the meaning of all safety symbols used in this book. Know how to respond to each symbol.

report any accident, incident, or hazard to your teacher immediately. Even if such an incident seems trivial, be sure to report it right away. Any incident involving bleeding, burns, fainting, chemical exposure, or ingestion should also be reported to your school nurse or school physician.

do not eat or drink, and do not apply cosmetics. Never store food in the laboratory. Wash your hands at the conclusion of each laboratory Investigation and before leaving the laboratory.

treat laboratory animals and plants cautiously and with respect. Always follow your teacher's directions for the proper care of live specimens. Remember to protect the safety of laboratory animals and plants as well as your own safety when you work with them.

clean your work area. When you have finished your work, follow your teacher's directions for cleanup and disposal of all laboratory materials.

ORGANIZING DATA

Data are records of facts and findings obtained from an Investigation. The type of data collected depends on the Investigation. For example, it may be a set of notes made during laboratory measurements; or even diagrams, drawings, or photographs. No matter which type of data it is, it must be collected, recorded, and analyzed carefully to ensure accurate results.

To collect good data, start by gathering all necessary equipment. Usually, you will want a clipboard with paper, a pencil, and any data sheets provided in the description of the Investigation.

When recording data, there are several important practices to keep in mind. First, always label your data appropriately. Labeling ensures that your experimental findings can be easily understood by you or anyone else. One important kind of labeling involves measurements. When making measurements, *always* record the units you are using. A measurement of "5" is incomplete; "5 cm" is much clearer. Another general rule is to record *all* your data. Even if data appear to be wrong, they are important. Discoveries are sometimes made by analyzing apparent inconsistencies in data. Most often, data that seem to be "wrong" are the result of experimental error; so if you obtain suspicious data, record them and then check to see that you are doing the experiment properly.

DATA TABLES

Data tables are probably the most common means of recording data. Prepared data tables are sometimes available in laboratory manuals, but it is important that you be able to construct your own. One way to do this is to choose a title for your data table and then make a list of the types of data to be collected. This list will become the headings for your data columns. For example, if you collected data on plant growth that included both the length of time it took for the plant to grow and the amount of growth, you could record your data in a table like the one shown in **Figure A.** Note that the units of measurement are provided in the column headings. Make all data tables you will need before running your experiment and starting to gather your data.

Figure A

Plant Growth Data	
Time (days)	Height of plant (cm)
1	10
3	12
5	15
7	18
9	20

GRAPHS

After you have recorded your laboratory data, you must determine how to display it. A table may serve this purpose, but graphs are sometimes better. Graphs represent information in a pictorial form that can often be interpreted "at a glance." Two types of graphs that are commonly used are the line graph and the bar graph.

Line Graphs

In a line graph, the data are arranged so that variables are represented as a single point. A straight line is then drawn through all of the data points. For example, the line graph shown in **Figure B** is easily constructed from the data in the plant growth table. The first step is to draw and label the axes. The horizontal axis usually represents the *independent variable*. The independent variable is the variable whose values are chosen by the experimenter. In the plant growth experiment, time is the independent variable. The vertical axis of a line graph is usually reserved for the *dependent variable*. The dependent variable has values that are determined by the independent variable. In the line graph below, the height of the plant depends on time, so plant height is the dependent variable.

Next, you must choose a scale for each of the axes. Choose the scales so that the graph takes up as much of the paper as possible because large graphs are much easier to read than small ones. The scales should feature wide intervals that are evenly spaced. Be sure to label the axes with the variables plotted. For example, notice how the axes have been labeled in **Figure B.**

After the axes have been drawn, scaled, and labeled, the data points are plotted. To plot each data point, lightly draw a horizontal line from the value on the vertical axis extending into the graph. Then draw a vertical

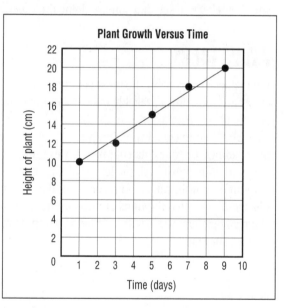

Figure B

line from the value on the horizontal axis extending into the graph. Where these two lines intersect, mark the data point. Once all the data points are drawn, draw the line that best fits through them. Remember that you do not "connect the dots" when you draw a line graph; instead, you draw the line between them that is as close to the points as possible. This best-fit line may not include every point in the data, but you should ensure that the average distance from the points to the line is as small as possible.

Finally give your line graph a brief title. Usually, the title should say how the variables are related to one another.

Bar Graphs

Bar graphs, or *histograms,* are convenient visual aids for comparing values of the same category. A bar graph is shown in **Figure C.** This graph compares the amount of water consumed for various purposes each day in the United States. The first steps in making a bar graph are similar to those for the line graph. You must choose your axes and label them. The independent variable remains on the horizontal axis, and the dependent variable is on the vertical axis. However, instead of plotting points on the graph, represent values of the dependent variable as a bar. Finally, title your bar graph.

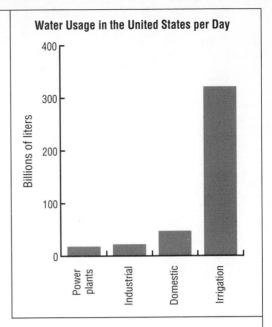

Figure C

DIAGRAMS

If your data are not numerical, they cannot be put into a table or graphed. Frequently, the best way to represent this type of information is to draw and label it. To do this, simply draw what you see, including all the features that you think are important, and then label as many parts or structures as possible. This technique is especially useful when conducting observations. For example, if you were interested in recording the foot adaptations of birds you observe in a wetlands habitat, you could diagram them as shown in **Figure D** below.

There are several things to remember as you make your diagrams or scientific drawings.

1. Make drawings large enough to be easily studied.
2. Drawings should show the spacing between parts of the specimen in proportion to its actual appearance. Size relationships are important in understanding and interpreting observations.
3. Label your drawings clearly and neatly. Lines drawn from labels to corresponding parts should be straight, so be sure to use a ruler. Label lines should never cross each other.
4. Be sure to title all drawings. Someone who looks at your drawings should be able to identify the specimen. Remember, neatness and accuracy are the most important parts of any diagram—you don't have to be an artist to make useful scientific drawings.

Figure D

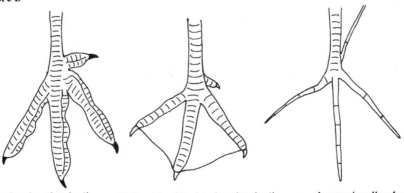

Coot (lobed swimming foot)   Mallard (webbed swimming foot)   Jacana (wading foot)

INVESTIGATION 1.1

SCIENTIFIC INVESTIGATIONS

The job of a scientist is to observe and explain the natural world. Many observations do not have an obvious explanation, so scientists generate hypotheses, or potential explanations, and test them with experiments.

A good scientist considers all the factors that might be responsible for what he or she observes. Factors that can vary and that we can measure are called *variables*. Examples of variables include temperature, time, water level, number of organisms, and so on. We can investigate the role of a specific variable by keeping all other variables constant while changing the variable we are testing and then observing what happens. This process is called a *controlled experiment*. For example, we might hypothesize that fish swim slowly at night because the water becomes cool. In a controlled experiment, we would examine the swimming speed of fish at different temperatures. The variable that we change, in this case water temperature, is called the *independent variable*. The variable that we think is affected by the independent variable, in this case swimming speed, is called the *dependent variable*. We could also hypothesize that fish swim more slowly at night because it's dark, and we would then examine the influence of light level (an independent variable) on swim speed (the dependent variable).

MATERIALS

- solution of yeast, corn syrup, and water
- 3 large test tubes (20 mm × 200 mm)
- #2 one-hole stoppers (3)
- 3 rubber or plastic delivery tubes
- 400 mL beakers (3)
- 100 mL beakers (3)
- ice cubes
- thermometer
- clock
- graph paper

THINK ABOUT IT

1. Why don't scientists try to test many variables in a single experiment?

_____

_____

WRITING HYPOTHESES

Hypotheses are critical to scientific investigation because they form the bases of our experimental design. Writing good hypotheses can be trickier than you think. We can make a number of statements about fish swimming speed that can be interpreted in different ways by changing just a few words. For example, consider the following:

- Fish swam slowly last night.

- Cold temperatures caused fish to swim slowly last night.

- Fish swimming speed is influenced by temperature: at cool nighttime temperatures they swim more slowly than at warmer daytime temperatures.

Each statement includes references to fish swim speed and temperature. However, each statement has its own meaning and only one can be considered a hypothesis. The first is not a hypothesis because rather than stating an explanation, it simply states two facts: (1) fish swam slowly and (2) it was nighttime.

The second is also not a hypothesis because although it is an explanation about what happened (fish swam slowly *because* it was cool); it states this explanation as an indisputable fact and is therefore not **testable.** Only the last statement is a hypothesis. It proposes an explanation for the swim speed of fish at night (temperatures are cooler), and it is testable because we can put fish in water of different temperatures and observe their swim speed.

A good hypothesis clearly states what variable we want to test and predicts its effect. It is not important if your hypothesis turns out to be right or wrong. What matters is that you can test it and draw an appropriate conclusion based on your data.

CONVERTING QUESTIONS TO HYPOTHESES

Below are some questions about the environment. Read them, and identify what variables can be controlled (independent) and what variables will be observed (dependent). Rewrite each question as a hypothesis. Double-underline the independent variable, and single underline the dependent variable. Your hypothesis should clearly state the predicted response of the dependent variable when the independent variable is manipulated. The independent variable can be increased, decreased, or even removed during the experiment.

For example, the question, "Is the <u>rate</u> at which a substances gains or loses heat related to its <u>density</u>?" can be restated as the hypothesis, "The more dense a substance is, the faster it will gain heat." Other possibilities are equally valid (for example, "the more dense a substance is, the more slowly it will gain heat," etc.)

2. Question: How does the amount of energy that hits the Earth in the form of light rays relate to the angle at which those rays strike (latitude)?

   _____

   _____

3. Question: Does rainfall influence the distribution of different biomes such as deserts, grasslands, and forests?

   _____

   _____

4. Question: Does the extinction of a predator species result in a faster rate of population growth in the prey species?

   _____

   _____

5. Question: Is plant cover related to soil erosion?

   _____

PUTTING HYPOTHESES TO WORK

Let's investigate a scientific question by making a hypothesis and conducting an experiment that tests your hypothesis. Yeast is a common microorganism that plays an important role in making bread. Yeast obtains energy to live by converting sugar to alcohol and carbon dioxide in a process called *fermentation*. According to a bread recipe, you dissolve a package of yeast in warm water and add flour, corn syrup, salt, and oil. The bread dough is kneaded several times and then left in a warm place to rise before being baked in a hot oven.

6. The question of interest is, "What does temperature have to do with fermentation by yeast?" Restate this question as a hypothesis.

_____

_____

EXPERIMENT DESIGN AND PROCEDURE

Your team will set up three test tubes containing yeast, water, and corn syrup stoppered with a gas-delivery tube. By placing the end of the delivery tube underwater, you can count the gas bubbles given off by the yeast. Each test tube of yeast will be in a water bath of different temperature. Tube A will be in a water bath cooled by a few ice cubes, tube B will be in room-temperature water, and tube C will be in a warm water bath.

7. Assemble the apparatus, and allow it to sit for 5 minutes so that the air pressure has time to stabilize. After the 5 minute pause, place the open end of the delivery tube underwater and begin to collect data on gas production. For the next 10 minutes keep count of the number of gas bubbles released from each tube, and record your counts in the table below.

8. Prepare a graph of the data using time on the *x*-axis and the total of gas bubbles released on the *y*-axis. Plot three curves on the same graph and label each with the temperature you recorded for each test tube. Compare your graph with that of at least one other team before handing in your report.

Carbon Dioxide Bubbles Released by Yeast										
Time (min.)	1	2	3	4	5	6	7	8	9	10
Tube A: ____ °C										
Tube B: ____ °C										
Tube C: ____ °C										

INTERPRETATIONS AND CONCLUSIONS

9. Which set of conditions is most similar to the conditions for the bread dough in the recipe? Why were two other conditions used in this experiment?

_____

_____

_____

_____

10. Why should you compare your results with those of other teams before writing your conclusion?

_____

_____

_____

11. What was the independent variable in this experiment? Why?

_____

12. What was the dependent variable in this experiment? Why?

_____

_____

13. Write a conclusion for this experiment. Describe how the independent and dependent variables are related. Tell how the data supports this conclusion.

_____

_____

_____

14. What does temperature have to do with making bread dough rise?

_____

_____

15. Science is not just something you know but also something you do. Explain this statement in light of what you have learned in this investigation.

_____

_____

_____

I N V E S T I G A T I O N

1.2

THE SECRET OF THE SCIENTIFIC METHOD

The scientific method can seem like something strange and mysterious—a special ritual used by people in white lab coats. But here is the secret behind the scientific method: It's really just a method of problem solving based on everyday life. You have been using the scientific method without even knowing it.

The steps of the scientific method include:

- observing and doing background research
- hypothesizing and predicting
- experimenting
- organizing and interpreting data
- forming a conclusion

Let's look in on a normal morning at the Hectic household. Tom Hectic is leaving for school, or at least trying to. The clock is showing 8:05 A.M., only 15 minutes before the tardy bell rings at Tom's school. As he frantically searches in his pockets and backpack Tom exclaims, "I can't find my house key! I can't leave without it! I'll get detention until I graduate! Mom, have you seen my key anywhere?"

"No, dear," comes his mother's calm reply.

"It's got to be in the pocket of the jeans I wore yesterday. Have you washed the clothes yet?" Tom shouts to his mother.

After getting another no for an answer, Tom sprints to his room and starts rummaging through a pile of dirty clothes. After looking in the pockets of the jeans in the pile, Tom still can't find his key. Then he wonders if the jeans he wore yesterday might be in the laundry room, so goes there, collects all the jeans, and searches the pockets of each pair.

"Aaaargh!" Tom yells in frustration. "It's not here. Maybe I left it in the key jar by the front door."

TOM'S SCIENTIFIC METHOD

1. What is Tom's initial observation, and what question or problem does it address?

_____

_____

2. What background research does Tom do regarding his initial observation?

_____

_____

3. What hypothesis does Tom make to explain his observation? How do we know that this is a hypothesis and not a conclusion?

_____

_____

_____

4. Describe Tom's experiment. Does it look like what you usually think of as a scientific experiment?

_____

_____

_____

5. How does Tom organize his data?

_____

_____

6. After Tom completes his experiment, what conclusion does he reach?

_____

_____

_____

7. What does Tom do next? Do you think that scientists do the same thing when their experiments do not confirm their hypotheses? Why?

_____

_____

_____

_____

_____

_____

I N V E S T I G A T I O N

2.1

IT TAKES GUTS!

Animals that eat grasses and wood really have guts—huge, industrial-strength guts! A large *gut,* which is another word for intestinal tract, is helpful for digesting cellulose, the main component of fibrous plants. Like starch, cellulose is a long chain of glucose (sugar) molecules linked together by chemical bonds. While most kinds of organisms can digest starch, only a few can digest cellulose. Why? The glucose molecules in starch all face one direction, while the glucose molecules in cellulose alternate in opposite directions. Organisms that can break the molecular bond responsible for the alternating arrangement can access the energy stored in cellulose. Such organisms include some species of fungi, protists, and bacteria.

You have probably heard of the wood-eating insects known as termites. Although termites eat wood, they cannot digest cellulose by themselves. So they get help from an amazing community of microorganisms that live in their gut. This arrangement is good for both parties: termites chew up the wood and deliver it to the microbes in their gut; the microbes in turn extract energy from the wood and supply some of it back to the termites. If a termite's microbial helpers were removed or killed, the termite would eventually starve because it could no longer obtain energy from its food. In this Investigation you will extract and observe some of the diverse microbes that live in a termite's gut.

MATERIALS

- live termites
- microscope
- slides
- coverslips
- tweezers
- saline solution
- petroleum jelly
- latex gloves

Termite

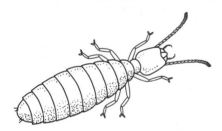

Cross section of termite and guts

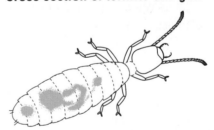

PROCEDURE

1. Place a drop of saline solution on a slide.

2. Use a pair of tweezers to pick up a termite and hold its hindquarters in the drop of saline. Gently squeeze the termite with the tweezers. This will induce the termite to excrete a small amount of intestinal fluid into the saline. Replace the termite in its container.

3. Rub a small amount of petroleum jelly on a piece of paper. Scrape all four edges of a coverslip over the petroleum jelly so that a small amount lines the outer edge of the coverslip. Place the coverslip over the drop of saline, and gently press out visible air bubbles. This procedure makes an airtight seal around the slide. This keeps the microorganisms on the slide alive because they are anaerobic, meaning that they need an oxygen-free environment to live.

4. Observe the gut contents under the microscope, moving from low power to high power and back again. How many different kinds of microorganisms can you see?

_____

_____

5. In the space below, draw pictures of at least two different kinds of micro-organism that you observe on the slide.

6. How do you think each of the organisms that you drew moves around?

_____

_____

7. What do you call the kind of relationship between the termite and its microbes? Who benefits from this relationship, and how?

_____

_____

8. What might happen if microorganisms similar to the ones in the termite also lived in your gut?

_____

_____

9. What might the effect of different environments (chemicals, gases, temperature) have on the microbes? How could you find out?

_____

_____

_____

INVESTIGATION 2.2

MISBEHAVING MEALWORMS?

Behavior is the way an animal acts. Observing the responses of an animal to various cues or stimuli tells us a great deal about the animal's behavior. For example, if a lizard perches on twigs in its terrarium, it is reasonable to guess that it is an arboreal lizard and that it therefore naturally spends much of its life perched in the branches of bushes or trees.

In this Investigation you will study the behavior of mealworms. Despite their name and appearance, mealworms are not worms; they are the larval stage of grain beetles. Adult grain beetles are black and shiny, but as larvae they look like small armored worms.

You will manipulate the environment of mealworms in various ways and observe the reactions of the mealworms. You will then use your observations to better understand the natural behavior of these larvae.

MATERIALS

- mealworms
- dissecting pan
- 150 mL beaker
- cornflakes
- bran flakes
- sweet cereal
- white paper
- aluminum foil
- transparent tape
- scissors
- small paintbrush
- index card
- desk lamp with an adjustable beam (optional)

SET THE STAGE

1. First create a circular arena in which to observe the mealworms' behavior. Use scissors to cut a sheet of plain white paper to fit the bottom of a dissecting pan. Tape the sheet into the pan, making sure that all edges are taped down, so the mealworms can't crawl under the paper. Trace a circle around the bottom of a 150 mL beaker in the center of the paper. Why is it important to draw a behavioral arena?

_____

_____

SOME LIKE IT DARK

2. Fit a piece of aluminum foil tightly across the top of one half of the dissecting pan. Arrange the pan so that the uncovered side is well lighted but the covered side is as dark as possible. You can do this easier if you have a desk lamp with an adjustable beam.

3. Fold an index card in half lengthwise and then open it up so that it can be used as a scoop. With a small paintbrush carefully brush 10 mealworms onto the card and transfer them to a 150 mL beaker. Pour them all at once into the circle at the bottom of your pan. Arrange the mealworms around the outer edge of the circle, and space them apart as evenly as possible. Observe the mealworms for 5–10 minutes.

4. How many mealworms moved into the lighted area? into the shaded area? What light conditions appear to be preferred by the mealworms?

_____

5. Are the mealworms bunched up or spread out? Where in the pan did they end up?

_____

LET THEM EAT FLAKES

6. Transfer the mealworms back to the beaker, and remove the aluminum foil. Make four piles of material (one pile each of white paper pieces, bran flakes, cornflakes, and sweet cereal) at equally spaced points around the circle. Which pile do you think the mealworms will prefer? Why?

_____

_____

7. Brush one mealworm at a time into the circle. Observe each mealworm for one minute before adding another. Record how many mealworms visit each pile. Also make a note if a mealworm does not visit any pile for a full minute.

8. Once all the mealworms are in the tray, observe their activity for 10 minutes and, continue to record their visits to the piles.

Food Preferences of Mealworms		
Location	Initial tally	Final tally
Bran flakes	_____	_____
Cornflakes	_____	_____
Sweet cereal	_____	_____
Paper	_____	_____
No pile	_____	_____

9. Which pile was most preferred by the mealworms?

_____

10. How do you think mealworms' behavior helps them survive?

_____

_____

I N V E S T I G A T I O N

3.1

DISSECTING OWL PELLETS

Owls are not known as finicky eaters. They prey on almost any animal that is small enough to be swallowed whole. Like many other birds, owls have an interesting adaptation: a special structure that prevents the indigestible parts of their prey—fur, feathers, bones, and so on—from passing into their intestines. These indigestible parts are shunted to a storage pouch, where they accumulate. A few hours after consuming a meal, the owl coughs up the accumulated indigestible material, which has been compressed into a pellet. Examining such a pellet can tell you what the owl ate. An examination of the remains of the owl's prey can give you a good idea of what the prey ate. Using this information, you can construct a simple food chain of the owl's environment.

MATERIALS

- owl pellet
- dissecting tools (such as toothpicks or tweezers)
- disposable gloves
- egg cartons
- small animal identification field guide with skull illustrations

THE TELLTALE PELLET

1. Working in groups of three or four, examine an owl pellet. Separate the fur or feathers from the bones. Identify the major components of the pellet.

2. If the pellet contains remains from more than one organism, determine as best as you can how many animals and species are present.

3. Attempt to group the remains by organism. Then try to assemble complete skeletons. Sample skeletal diagrams are shown below.

4. Closely examine the skulls of the prey animals. Compare them to the diagrams of skulls on the next page. To what purpose do the teeth or bills seem most suited—tearing flesh, chewing plant parts, or grinding seeds? If you are able to identify the prey animals, find out their usual food sources.

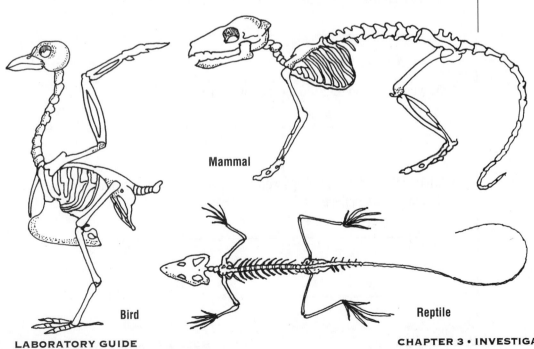

Mammal

Bird

Reptile

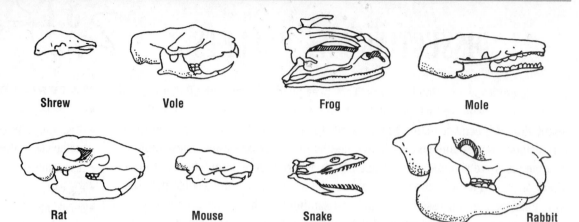

Shrew   Vole   Frog   Mole

Rat   Mouse   Snake   Rabbit

5. On a separate piece of paper, construct a simple food chain based on your findings.

6. Compare your findings with those of other students.

ANALYZE YOUR FINDINGS

7. What kinds of animals did you identify in the owl pellet?

_____

_____

_____

_____

8. Compare your findings with those of your classmates using the following questions:

a. What animals were represented most often in the pellets?

_____

_____

b. What common traits do these animals have?

_____

_____

9. What biological relationships were you able to determine from your examination of the owl pellets?

_____

_____

_____

INVESTIGATION 3.2

THE CARBON CYCLE

Carbon, a chemical element, is a component of nearly all biological molecules. Carbon is found in all organisms, where it is one of the main components of cells. Organisms get energy from carbon compounds. Organisms obtain carbon from their environment. Plants get carbon through photosynthesis, while animals get carbon by eating plants or by eating organisms that ate plants. Think of the food you eat—it mostly consists of parts or products of living organisms. Consider a slice of pizza. The crust is made from wheat, which is part of a plant; the sauce is made from tomatoes, the fruit of a different plant; and the cheese is made from milk, an animal product. All of these animal and plant products supply you with the carbon compounds you need to live and grow.

So what do organisms do with carbon compounds? Through a process called *cellular respiration,* the cells of most organisms use oxygen to release the energy that is stored in food molecules. Fungi use a different process, called *fermentation,* that does not use oxygen to release energy. During both cellular respiration and fermentation, energy is released when the chemical bonds that hold the food molecules together are broken. All organisms then use elements, such as carbon, to build their own biological molecules. The molecules left after these processes are waste products.

One of the waste products is carbon dioxide, a molecule that contains carbon. As organisms conduct cellular respiration or fermentation, they release waste carbon dioxide as a gas into the atmosphere. Photosynthetic organisms, such as plants, absorb this carbon dioxide and use it in photosynthesis. The carbon gets incorporated into parts of the plant (for example, as part of the starch in a potato) and may end up being consumed by yet another animal. The constant cycling of carbon through organisms to the atmosphere and back again is called the *carbon cycle.*

MATERIALS

- bakers yeast (check expiration date)
- 0.5 g sugar
- warm water
- 0.5 g salt
- 50 mL beakers (3)
- 100 mL beaker

THINK ABOUT IT

1. What kinds of organisms use carbon in the creation of cells?

_____

2. What happens to the carbon you eat but do not use in the creation of cells?

_____

PROBLEM

In this experiment you will be working with yeast, a single-celled organism that is a fungus. Yeast obtains energy from food through the process of fermentation. By providing the yeast with different sources of food, we will answer the following question: What substance is used by yeast as a source of energy?

PROCEDURE

3. To prepare a yeast solution, add 1 g of dry baker's yeast to 100 mL of very warm water, and stir the mixture gently.

4. Label three beakers 1, 2, and 3, and fill each half full with yeast solution.

5. Dissolve 0.5 g of sugar in beaker 2 and 0.5 g of salt in beaker 3.

6. Note what happens in each beaker, and record your observations in the data table. Be sure to look for bubbles rising to form a foamy layer. **This is evidence of carbon dioxide production.** Be sure to use your sense of smell also!

Reaction of Yeast to Different Food Sources	
Beaker	**Observations**
1	
2	
3	

ANALYZE YOUR OBSERVATIONS

7. Which beaker served as the control in this experiment?

_____

8. What food sources were tested in this experiment?

_____

Below are the word and chemical equations for the fermentation carried out by yeast cells.

$$\text{sugar} \xrightarrow{\text{enzymes}} \text{energy} + \text{alcohol} + \text{carbon dioxide}$$

$$C_6H_{12}O_6 \xrightarrow{\text{enzymes}} \text{energy} + 2C_2H_5OH + 2CO_2$$

9. Did you notice a smell of alcohol in any beaker, and if so, which one? What does this mean?

_____

10. In which of the beakers did you notice bubbling, and what does this mean?

_____

11. Based on the equations on the previous page and on what you observed, in which of the beakers do you think the process of fermentation occurred?

_____

12. Why didn't fermentation happen in all of the beakers?

_____

_____

13. What would you conclude is the source of the carbon in the carbon dioxide produced?

_____

14. Below is a diagram that shows the path of carbon in the carbon cycle. Fill in the blanks to describe what is happening during each of the steps.

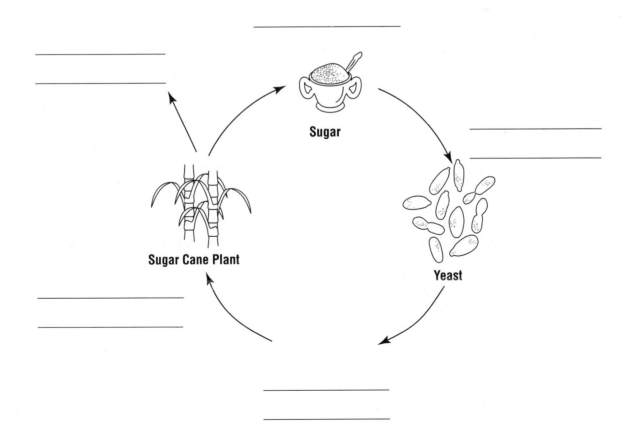

15. Think about a sugar-based food that you commonly eat, such as bread. When you eat it, how do you become a part of the cycle we see on the last page? In the space provided below, draw another diagram of the carbon cycle in which you are one of the organisms involved. Describe what is happening at each step.

16. How is burning gas in a car similar to digestion in living organisms?

_____

_____

_____

_____

17. Sugar acts as a fuel for living organisms. Gasoline, which comes from the remains of dead plants, provides the fuel for cars. Why is there so much stored energy in these fuels?

_____

_____

_____

_____

INVESTIGATION 3.3

A SUCCESSION OF MICROBES

In natural communities, the replacement of species that occurs over time is called succession. It may be caused by several different factors, including competition, changing resources, or one species creating resources for species that follow. The newer species thrive and may dominate the community, but they are eventually replaced by still other species until a stable climax community forms. Succession is especially noticeable after natural disasters or severe disturbances caused by humans.

In this Investigation you will study succession in two communities of microscopic organisms living in wet soil. You will place each of your communities in a Winogradsky column, a device that was originally developed by Russian microbiologist Sergei N. Winogradsky in the 1880s. You will add various nutrients to one of the columns. The other column will be your control, and you will not add anything to it. By comparing the experimental Winogradsky column with the control, you will study the effects of added nutrients on microbial succession.

BUILD WINOGRADSKY COLUMNS

1. Remove any hard lumps, twigs, rocks, and other large particles from about 1,000 cu. cm of soil. Strain soil through a sieve to remove any remaining large particles. Separate the soil into two equal piles.

2. Add a small handful of well-shredded newspaper, half of a crushed eggshell, and about one-quarter of the crumbled yolk from a hard-boiled egg to one of the piles of soil. The newspaper, eggshell, and egg yolk provide organic material, calcium carbonate, and sulfate, respectively, for various microbial populations. Mix the nutrients thoroughly with the soil.

3. Label the two plastic bottles. Label one as the control and the other as the experimental bottle.

4. Using the funnel, gently pour the soil that contains added nutrients into the experimental bottle to a height of about 5 cm. Then gently pour the soil without added nutrients into the control bottle. Use the dowel to pack the soil into the bottom of each bottle and to remove the air trapped in the soil. Add a little more soil and a few spoonfuls of pond water to each bottle, using the dowel again to pack the soil and release any trapped air. Repeat this process until the level of the soil is about 5 cm from the top of each bottle. Add water up to about 2 cm from the top of each bottle, and cap the bottles tightly.

5. Place your Winogradsky columns in an area where they will receive indirect sunlight over the next six weeks.

WATCH WHAT HAPPENS

6. Make colored sketches of the columns and their contents once a week for 6 weeks in the table on the next page.

MATERIALS

- 500 mL clear plastic soda bottles with screw-on caps (2)
- 1,000 cu. cm soil from a natural area
- sieve
- dowel (for packing the soil in the bottles)
- funnel
- spoon
- fresh water from a naturally occurring source (such as a pond)
- small handful of shredded newspaper
- one-half eggshell, crushed
- one-quarter crumbled hard-boiled egg yolk
- metric ruler
- colored pencils
- wax pencil

Sketches of Winogradsky Columns

Week	1	2	3	4	5	6
Control column						
Experimental column						

ANALYSIS

7. Use the following key to describe the succession in microbe populations that you observed in the experimental bottle over the course of the 6 weeks.

>**Green clumps:** algae

>**Black spots:** sulfate-reducing bacteria

>**Reddish purple spots:** purple sulfur bacteria

>**Rust-colored areas:** purple nonsulfur bacteria

Also describe evidence of any other populations you may have observed.

_____

_____

_____

_____

_____

_____

_____

_____

8. What differences did you observe between the two columns in terms of the rate and pattern of succession?

_____

_____

_____

_____

_____

_____

_____

_____

9. A simple sulfur cycle is going on inside the columns. The sulfate-reducing bacteria produce a substance called hydrogen sulfide (the black spots), which is used by the purple sulfur bacteria for photosynthesis. The purple sulfur bacteria then produce other forms of sulfur, which are used by the sulfate-reducing bacteria.

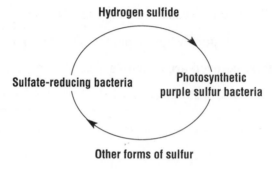

Hydrogen sulfide

Sulfate-reducing bacteria

Photosynthetic
purple sulfur bacteria

Other forms of sulfur

Given this information, what could you do to stop this sulfur cycle?

_____

_____

_____

10. What could have caused the succession in your bottle, and how is it different from the succession in a natural ecosystem?

_____

_____

_____

_____

_____

EXTENSIONS

You may want to try these variations and observe their effects on microbial succession in your Winogradsky columns.

- Add various pollutants (such as fertilizer or insecticide) to your column.

- Keep your column on ice or next to a heating vent.

- Expose your column to different intensities of light (direct sunlight, total darkness, etc.).

- Use different combinations of soil and water from various sources.

- Use different sources of nutrients, such as sawdust, fruit and vegetable peels, or crushed seashells.

I N V E S T I G A T I O N

4.1

CLIMATIC ADAPTATIONS

The plant and animal species living in a biome adapt to their climate. In turn they modify the climate through their participation living in each biome in the water cycle. The climate of each biome varies, and the plants and animals living in each biome must be able to tolerate this variation to survive. For example, deer living in a high-altitude forest must be able to survive the dry summer as well as the cold winter.

Some biomes have more variable climates than others, so you might assume that species from the more variable biomes can tolerate larger differences in temperature and precipitation than species from the less variable biomes. Is this assumption correct? Do plants from different climates respond differently to climate? In this experiment you will explore one climatic variable: temperature. So turn up the heat, and let's get growing.

MATERIALS

- 12 Petri dishes
- various seeds
- filter paper
- sealable plastic bags
- incubator
- refrigerator
- marking pens

HYPOTHESIZE

1. Read the experimental design below, and identify the independent and dependent variables. Think about how they might be related and what might happen when the independent variable is changed. Write a hypothesis that expresses your prediction.

_____

_____

DESIGN AN EXPERIMENT

2. Obtain seeds from at least two plant species that prefer warm environments and at least two plant species that prefer cool environments. Some suggestions for warm weather species include watermelon, pumpkin, cucumber, and squash. Varieties that prefer cool weather include lettuce, celery, spinach, endive, radish, beet, turnip, and parsnip.

3. Set up a series of germination tests for each variety. Line 12 Petri dishes (plastic or glass with lids) with two or three sheets of wet filter paper.

4. Place 10 seeds of each selected variety to its own dish, and label the dishes accordingly. One will be kept in an incubator at 42°C, another will be kept at 22°C (room temperature), and the third dish will be kept in a refrigerator for 16 hours per day and at room temperature for 8 hours per day.

5. Seal all dishes together in a sealable plastic bag to prevent drying out and keep the dishes at their prescribed temperatures over the next 10 days. Observe daily.

6. Record the number of seeds that sprout roots and shoots in the data table below. Note which (root or shoot) emerges first and how many emerge. Also note if any seeds die or become infected with mold. After 10 days, combine all class data, and proceed to the analysis portion of this experiment.

Seed Germination Success			
Cool-weather seeds	Alternating cool/ warm temps. 6° to 22°C	Warm temp. 22°C	Hot temp. 42°C
Warm-weather seeds			

ANALYSIS & CONCLUSIONS

7. Which seed varieties performed best in the cool environment?

_____

8. Which seed varieties performed best in the warm environment?

_____

9. Which seed varieties germinated in the widest temperature range?

_____

10. Which environment allowed the most seeds to germinate?

_____

11. Which seeds would do well in a tropical climate?

_____

12. Does temperature affect the germination of seeds? Explain.

_____

_____

_____

_____

INVESTIGATION

4.2

FACTORS THAT INFLUENCE ECOSYSTEMS

MATERIALS
• transect grid
• ruler

Ecosystems are collections of plant and animal communities living in a specific set of environmental conditions. These conditions play an important role in determining what plants can live there. Because animals depend directly and indirectly on plants to live, the existence of certain plants partly determines what animals can live there. The Earth's major ecosystems, such as deserts, tropical rain forests, and taiga, are called *biomes*.

In the previous activity you learned that latitude has a strong influence on an area's temperature, resulting in polar, tropical, and temperate climates. However, a careful look at a map reveals that ecosystems at the same latitude often have different climates. Why? This activity will point you toward the answer.

THINK AHEAD

1. What factors account for differences in ecosystems found at the same latitude? Suggest some possible environmental factors that vary across the United States from San Francisco to Washington, D.C.

_____

_____

PROCEDURE

In this procedure you will test two hypotheses, one that relates differences in ecosystem vegetation to rainfall and another that relates differences in ecosystem vegetation to altitude. Complete the following sentences to form your two hypotheses.

2. Ecosystem distribution is related to precipitation; regions that receive a lot of precipitation are wet and therefore

_____

3. Ecosystem distribution is related to altitude; regions at higher altitudes are cold and therefore

_____

Look at the data table on the next page. The table lists major cities and weather stations between the latitudes 36°N and 41°N. It also lists the altitude, average annual precipitation, and ecosystem in each location. Plot altitude on the transect grid provided on page 25, and connect the points. Use the y-axis on the left side for your altitude scale. Plot the precipitation data on the same grid, connecting the points and using the scale on the right. You may also find it useful to label the location names. Your completed line graph will help you see any relationship between rainfall, altitude, and biome type.

Characteristics of Locations Across the U.S.			
	Distance from San Francisco	Altitude above sea level	Average rainfall in./yr.	Natural biome or ecosystem
San Francisco, CA	0	250'	23"	redwood forest
Sacramento, CA	100 mi.	26'	19"	grassland
Donner Pass, CA	200 mi.	7,000'	69"	coniferous forest
Reno, NV	250 mi.	4,400'	8"	cool desert
Salt Lake City, UT	650 mi.	4,200'	16"	cool desert
Loveland Pass, CO	900 mi.	11,000'	38"	coniferous forest
Denver, CO	950 mi.	5,325'	12"	short grass prairie
Topeka, KS	1,450 mi.	925'	34"	tall grass prairie
St. Louis, MO	1,750 mi.	567'	37"	broadleaf forest
Cincinnati, OH	2,100 mi.	488'	40"	broadleaf forest
Washington, DC	2,500 mi.	9'	39"	broadleaf forest

ANALYSIS

4. Is there a definite trend in precipitation levels from Denver to San Francisco or from Denver to Washington, D.C.? If so, describe it.

_____

_____

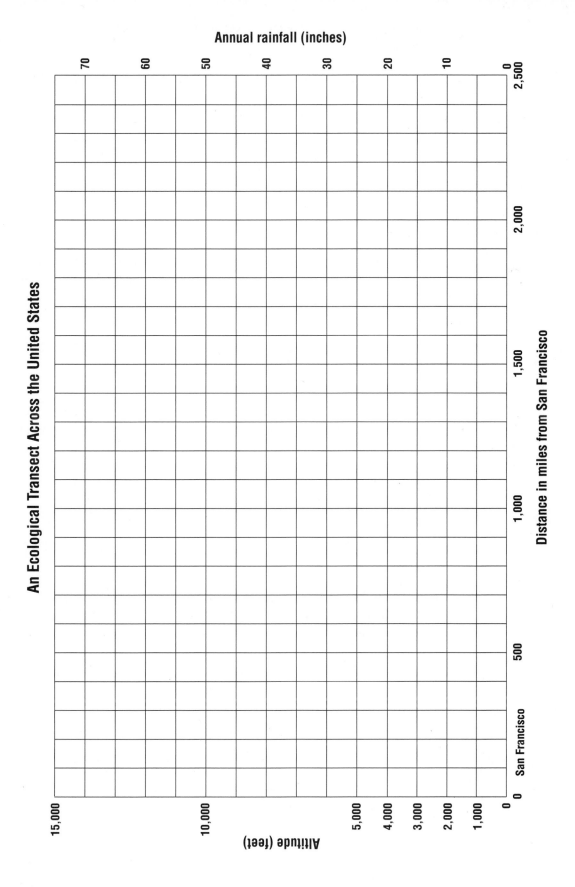

An Ecological Transect Across the United States

Annual rainfall (inches)

Distance in miles from San Francisco

Altitude (feet)

5. How do mountain ranges affect precipitation? Give an example that supports your answer.

_____

_____

_____

6. What kinds of ecosystems occur in areas of high and low precipitation?

_____

_____

7. Is precipitation level or altitude the more important factor in determining an area's ecosystem? Is there an interaction between these two factors? Explain.

_____

_____

_____

_____

8. Does the data support or refute your hypotheses about the effect of precipitation and altitude on an ecosystem type?

_____

_____

_____

_____

9. Refer to the world biome map (Figure 4-1) on page 79 in your textbook, and examine the ecosystem patterns of the Eurasian continent. What do you infer about the distribution of rainfall in Eurasia?

_____

_____

_____

_____

_____

I N V E S T I G A T I O N

A MATTER OF DEGREE

Consider the following familiar observations: (1) In areas with temperate climates, as in most of the United States, daily temperatures change dramatically with the seasons. (2) The position of the sun in the sky changes with the seasons. For example, in summer the sun is almost directly overhead at midday, while in winter it is closer to the horizon. (3) If you travel at least 300 mi. north or south to a different latitude, the climate changes. Areas near the equator generally have warm climates, and those near the poles generally have cool climates. How can we explain these observations? In other words, what causes the differences in temperature that accompany changes in season and changes in latitude?

FORM A HYPOTHESIS

1. The observations above suggest a relationship between the position of the sun in the sky and the average temperature of the Earth's surface. Read the experimental design below. Identify the independent and dependent variables, and use them to propose a hypothesis about the relationship between the angle of the sun's rays and the Earth's temperature.

_____

_____

_____

EXPERIMENT

2. Obtain four cereal boxes of equal size, and remove the front panel from each box.

3. Line the inside of the boxes with black paper. Then cover the open sides with clear plastic wrap, and seal the edges with tape.

4. Arrange the lamps over three of the boxes so that the bulb is approximately 6 in. from the surface. Arrange the first lamp so that the light makes a 90° angle with the bottom of the first box (as in Diagram 1). Aim the second lamp at a 45° angle. Aim the third lamp at a 22.5° angle. Do not put a lamp above the fourth box. What is the purpose of the fourth box?

_____

_____

5. Turn on the lamps and note the temperature in each box every minute for 21 minutes. Record your data in Table 1.

MATERIALS
- 4 cereal boxes (small to medium sized)
- black paper
- clear plastic wrap
- thermometer (alcohol-type recommended)
- 3 gooseneck lamps with bulbs of 60 W or greater
- scissors
- tape
- protractor

Diagram 1

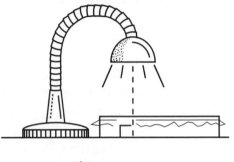

90° angle

45° angle

22.5° angle

Table 1

Temperature of Boxes Heated by Lights at Different Angles											
Time in min.:	0	1	2	3	4	5	6	7	8	9	10
Temperature in °C (light at 90° angle)											
Temperature in °C (light at 45° angle)											
Temperature in °C (light at 22.5° angle)											
Temperature in °C (no light)											

Table 1 (continued)

Temperature of Boxes Heated by Lights at Different Angles											
Time in min.:	11	12	13	14	15	16	17	18	19	20	21
Temperature in °C (light at 90° angle)											
Temperature in °C (light at 45° angle)											
Temperature in °C (light at 22.5° angle)											
Temperature in °C (no light)											

6. On a piece of graphing paper, make a line graph with the data from Table 1. Use the *x*-axis to record time and the *y*-axis to record temperature. Make sure to label each line with the appropriate lamp angle.

7. In which box did the greatest change in temperature occur?

   _____

8. In which box did the smallest change in temperature occur?

   _____

9. What do the differences between the slopes of the curves for each of the angles imply about the rate of heat gain?

   _____

10. Energy can change forms, such as when light is absorbed by an object and turned into heat, but energy cannot be lost; it must go somewhere. Since all the lamps gave off the same amount of energy, where did the energy go with respect to the boxes that never reached high temperatures?

    _____

    _____

11. What is your conclusion about the relationship between the angle of light and the temperature?

    _____

    _____

EXTENSION

12. How does the principle of the previous experiment apply to the Earth and its climatic zones? To demonstrate your understanding of this principle and its implications for the Earth, draw latitude lines for the Arctic Circle, the Tropic of Cancer, equator, the Tropic of Capricorn, and the Antarctic Circle on the diagram below. Label each line with its degree of latitude. Color the warmest zone yellow, and label it "Tropical Zone." Color the coolest zone blue, and label it "Polar Zone." Finally, color the remaining zone green, and label it "Temperate Zone."

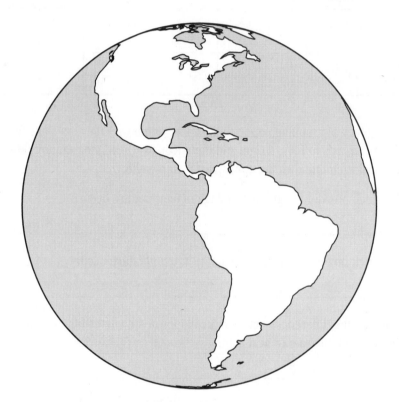

I N V E S T I G A T I O N 5.1

EUTROPHICATION: TOO MUCH OF A GOOD THING?

Plants depend on nutrients such as phosphates and nitrates to survive. However, when people release large amounts of these nutrients into rivers and lakes, artificial eutrophication can occur. In artificial eutrophication, nutrients cause algae and plant life to grow rapidly and then die off and decay. When microorganisms decompose the algae and plant matter, they use up oxygen in the water, causing the death of fish and other animals that depend on oxygen for survival. Eutrophication is commonly caused by phosphates, which are often found in detergents, and by nitrates, which are found in animal wastes and fertilizers. In this Investigation you will observe artificial eutrophication in an aquatic ecosystem.

MATERIALS
- 1 qt. jars (3)
- wax pencil
- distilled water
- fertilizer (household use)
- graduated cylinder
- stirring rod
- pond water containing viable organisms
- plastic wrap
- fluorescent lamp
- eyedropper
- microscope
- microscope slides with coverslips
- guide to pond life identification

| ***Spirogyra*** | ***Volvox*** | ***Daphnia*** | ***Vorticella*** |
| (producer) | (producer) | (consumer) | (consumer) |

Some common pond organisms

SET UP YOUR EXPERIMENT

1. Working with your team, use a wax pencil to label one jar "Control," a second jar "Fertilizer," and a third jar "Excess fertilizer."

2. Put 750 mL of distilled water in each of the three jars. Read the label on the fertilizer container to determine the recommended dilution of fertilizer for watering plants. To the "Fertilizer" jar, add the amount of fertilizer recommended for a quart of water. To the "Excess fertilizer" jar, add 10 times this amount of fertilizer. Stir the contents of each jar thoroughly to dissolve the fertilizer.

3. Obtain a sample of pond water. Stir it gently but thoroughly to ensure that the organisms in it are evenly distributed. Measure 100 mL of pond water into each of the three jars.

4. Cover each jar loosely with plastic wrap. Place all three jars about 20 cm away from a fluorescent lamp. (Do not place the jars in direct sunlight, as this may cause them to heat up too much.)

OBSERVE ECOSYSTEM CHANGES

5. Observe a drop of pond water under the microscope. In the space below, draw at least four of the organisms that you see. Determine whether the organisms you see are algae (usually green) or consumers (usually able to move). Describe the number and type of organisms that you see.

_____

_____

_____

_____

6. Based on your understanding of eutrophication, make a prediction about how the pond organisms will grow in each of the three jars.

_____

_____

_____

_____

7. Observe the jars when you first set them up and at least once every three days for the next 3 weeks. Note color, odor, and any visible presence of life-forms. Record your observations in the table on page 34.

8. When life-forms begin to be visible in the jars (probably after a week or two), use an eyedropper to remove a sample of organisms from each jar, and observe the sample under the microscope. How have the number and type of organisms changed? Record your observations below.

_____

_____

_____

_____

9. At the end of your 3-week observation period, once again remove a sample from each jar and observe it under the microscope. In the space provided, sketch at least four of the most abundant organisms and describe how the number and type of organisms have changed.

_____

_____

_____

ANALYZE YOUR RESULTS

10. After 3 weeks, which jar shows the most abundant growth of algae? What may have caused this growth?

_____

_____

11. Did you observe any effects on organisms other than algae in the jar with the most abundant algae growth? Explain.

_____

_____

_____

12. Did your observations match your predictions? Explain.

_____

_____

_____

13. How can artificial eutrophication be prevented in natural water bodies?

_____

_____

Name_____ Class_____ Date_____

Control			
Date	**Color**	**Odor**	**Other observations**

Fertilizer			
Date	**Color**	**Odor**	**Other observations**

Excess fertilizer			
Date	**Color**	**Odor**	**Other observations**

I N V E S T I G A T I O N 5.2

OPERATION OIL SPILL CLEANUP

Offshore oil drilling and the use of supertankers for transporting oil can lead to oil spills. Oil spills can damage fishing grounds, spoil beaches, kill marine birds and mammals, and destroy shellfish beds. A mere 1 gal. of oil can contaminate as much as 5 million gallons of water. Because you are concerned about these issues, you have chosen to work for Eco-Marine, Inc., an environmental remediation firm that specializes in solving ocean pollution problems. Your supervisor has distributed the following memo describing a new assignment.

M E M O

To: All Eco-Marine Staff
From: Marina Waters, President
Re: Oil Spill Cleanup Proposal

Mega Oil Company is accepting proposals for a cleanup plan that could be implemented in the event of an oil spill from one of their supertankers. There are several top-notch companies competing for this contract, so we need to work hard to show Mega that *we* can do the best job. We must develop a plan for a cleanup that is fast, effective, and minimally harmful to the environment.

Each work team will develop its own plan. First you will test cleanup materials, and then you will develop a complete cleanup plan. We will then test the plans and choose the best one to submit to Mega.

Marina Waters

MATERIALS:

- 100 mL vegetable oil
- 9 in. × 13 in. pan
- 2 shallow containers for water
- spoon
- small beaker
- sand (or gravel)
- pipe cleaners
- feathers
- watch (or clock)
- several of the following: spoons, craft sticks, toothpicks, dip nets, drinking straws, plastic wrap, aluminum foil, pieces of plastic foam, string, pieces of brown paper bag, cotton balls, pieces of nylon stocking, pieces of sponge, paper towels, coffee filters, cloth, wood shavings, sawdust, liquid detergent

TEST CLEANUP SUPPLIES

1. Work with a team of students as assigned by your teacher. From the materials list, select 5–10 supplies to use to clean up an oil spill.

2. Pour a spoonful of oil onto the surface of water in a shallow container to represent an oil spill in the open ocean. Pour a small amount of oil onto rocks, sand or gravel, pipe cleaners, and feathers in another container for testing cleanup of the shore and wildlife. (The pipe cleaners represent sea mammals, and the feathers represent birds.)

3. Test your supplies to determine their effectiveness in the following categories:

   - containing an oil spill
   - cleaning up the water and recovering spilled oil
   - cleaning up the shore and wildlife

   Also evaluate the environmental impact of using a large quantity of each of your cleaning supplies in the ocean.

Record your ratings of each material in the table below. Rate each material as poor, average, good, or excellent.

Evaluation of Cleaning Supplies					
Material	Containment	Water cleanup & oil recovery	Shore cleanup	Wildlife cleanup	Environmental impact

DEVISE A PLAN

4. Write complete directions for cleaning up an oil spill with the supplies you tested. You must specify materials and techniques for the following:

- containment of the oil spill
- cleanup of water and recovery of oil
- shore cleanup, including both rocks and sand
- wildlife cleanup and reintroduction into habitat (include birds, shore animals, and sea animals)
- minimizing the impact of your cleanup operations on the ocean ecosystem

_____

_____

_____

_____

_____

INVESTIGATION 5.2, CONTINUED

TEST YOUR PLAN

5. Build a model ocean in a 9 in. × 13 in. pan. Create a beach using sand or gravel and a few rocks at one end of the pan. Place a feather and a pipe cleaner at the shoreline. Add water carefully.

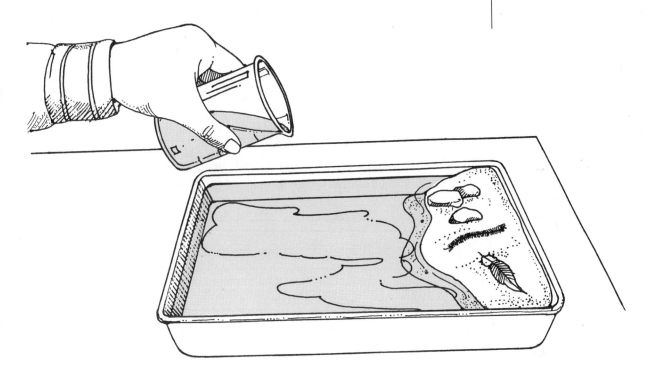

6. Let a small beaker of oil represent your supertanker. Spill 50 mL of oil into the center of your water area. Gently blow the oil toward the shore.

7. Implement your cleanup plan. Your goal is to complete the cleanup as quickly and effectively as possible. For each cleanup task (oil containment, oil recovery, shore cleanup, and wildlife cleanup), have a separate column to record the time it takes to complete the task and how well the cleanup works.

_____

_____

_____

_____

_____

_____

_____

INVESTIGATION 5.2, CONTINUED

TEAM DEBRIEFING

8. After all teams have finished their cleanup, present your results to the class. Take a class vote to determine whose plan should be submitted to Mega Oil Company.

9. What containment method worked best? How would weather affect the results?

_____

_____

_____

_____

10. Was it possible to recover any of the oil? Could the recovery methods that worked best be used in a real oil spill?

_____

_____

_____

_____

11. What happened when the oil reached the beach? How effective was cleanup of sand and wildlife?

_____

_____

_____

_____

12. What factors might make a real oil spill cleanup different from your simulation?

_____

_____

_____

13. In a real spill, what impact might cleanup methods have on plant and animal life?

_____

_____

_____

INVESTIGATION 6.1

TESTING ACID, TRACKING RAIN

There are two forms of air pollution, particulate and gaseous. Particulate pollution consists of small solid particles, like ash and soot. These particles are carried by wind currents until they settle out, after the wind has calmed. Gaseous pollution consists of chemical gases that are vaporized during combustion and industrial processes. The gases mix with air and sometimes chemically combine to form other substances. Oxides of nitrogen, sulfur, and carbon react with water vapor to form acids. When these acidic vapors condense into liquid droplets, the result is acid rain.

Acid rain has both direct and indirect effects on organisms. Direct effects include the death of aquatic plants and animals and the injury and death of trees that take up acidic water. Indirect effects include the leaching of aluminum from soil and the death of organisms that depend on organisms directly killed by acid rain.

The major source of sulfur and nitrogen oxides is the combustion of fossil fuels, including coal burned in power plants and gasoline burned in vehicles. Because these gaseous pollutants are airborne, they can easily travel hundreds of miles from their source before combining with water. In this Investigation you will test various substances for acidity and examine how acid rain is formed and distributed.

MATERIALS
- pH paper
- dropper pipet
- variety of solutions, from acid to base
- disposable soda straw
- Erlenmeyer flask
- yeast culture
- microscope

WHAT'S YOUR pH?

1. First you will learn how to measure acidity using the pH scale. pH is a measure of the number of free hydrogen ions in a solution. Ions are atoms or groups of atoms that have a positive or negative electrical change. Solutions with a low pH have many hydrogen ions (H^+) and are called *acidic*. Solutions with a high pH have few hydrogen ions and are called *basic*. Your teacher will give you a variety of common chemical solutions. Place a drop of each solution on a fresh piece of pH paper, match the resulting color to the pH scale, and identify the pH. List the substances and their pH below.

_____

_____

_____

_____

_____

2. How does your pH paper indicate an acid? a base? What color indicates a pH of 7?

_____

_____

3. Which of the substances you tested are strong acids? Which are strong bases?

_____

_____

4. Did you know that you can create acid by breathing? Carbon dioxide from your breath combines with water vapor in the air to form carbonic acid, H_2CO_3, which separates into H^+ and HCO_3^- in liquid. You will need a soda straw, an Erlenmeyer flask, distilled water, and pH paper. Check the pH of the distilled water and record it in the chart below. Gently blow through the straw into the water for 10 seconds. Check and record the water's pH again. Blow for 10 more seconds and record the pH. Repeat the procedure until you have exhaled through the water for 120 seconds. Be sure to pause and rest between each 10-second interval so that you do not hyperventilate and become dizzy.

pH of Water into Which You Exhale													
Time (sec.)	0	10	20	30	40	50	60	70	80	90	100	110	120
pH													

5. Describe the change in pH in the water when you exhaled. Did this form a strong or weak acid?

_____

6. Now you will determine how acid concentrations affect living microorganisms. First prepare a live yeast culture by placing 1 mL of the culture into 9 mL of water. Examine the yeast under a microscope to observe that the yeast cells are actively budding. Check the pH of the culture. Seven teams in your class will each add a solution of sulfuric acid, H_2SO_4, to their yeast tube, wait 10 minutes, and measure the pH. The first team will add 1 mL of 1 molar H_2SO_4 to their yeast culture. The second team will dilute the acid 10:1. The third team will dilute the acid twice, making it 100:1; the fourth team will dilute it three times, making it 1,000:1; the fifth team will dilute it four times, making it 10,000:1; the sixth team will dilute it five times, making it 100,000:1; and the seventh team will dilute it six times, making it 1,000,000:1. Record the pH values measured by each team in the table on the following page.

Response of Yeast to Increased Acidity							
	1 molar H2SO4	Diluted 10-1	Diluted 10-2	Diluted 10-3	Diluted 10-4	Diluted 10-5	Diluted 10-6
pH							
Yeast budding							

7. Describe how pH affects the microorganism yeast.

_____

_____

FIND THE RAIN'S FINGERPRINT

Rainwater normally has a pH of about 5.7. This is slightly more acidic than the pH of pure water, which is about 7. Acid rain has a pH of 5 or lower. By conducting pH tests and studying the distribution of acidified water bodies, you can trace acid rain to its source.

8. Using the information in the chart below, find areas with pH values of 5 or lower. Then mark these areas on the map on the following page. The prevailing winds in this area blow from west to east. Armed with this information, study the map and determine where you think the most likely source of the acid rain is, and mark the spot with an **X.** Draw an arrow on the map showing the direction that the acidic pollution travels from its source.

pH at Various Coordinates on the Map							
Coordinates	M2	U4	L8	Y10	G13	K15	S19	DD17
pH	7.4	7.2	7.3	7.3	7.3	7.0	7.1	7.1
Coordinates	Y22	EE22	N27	FF26	FF28	J22	J26	029
pH	6.7	4.9	6.2	4.7	4.8	7.3	6.8	5.0
Coordinates	U30	BB33	K35	K39	FF38	AA41	U38	F42
pH	4.5	5.0	6.0	6.5	5.8	6.0	5.5	6.7

Distribution of Acid Rain (pH)

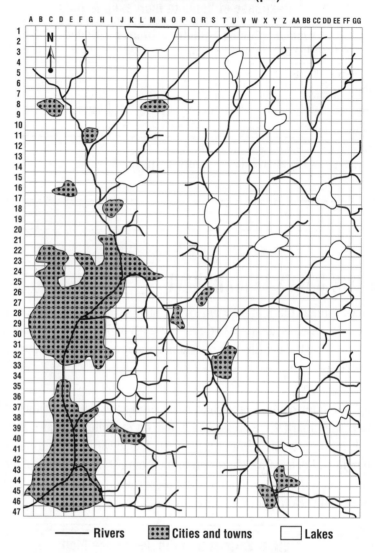

——— Rivers   ▒▒▒ Cities and towns   ☐ Lakes

9. Write a paragraph in which you identify the source of the air pollution and its general path through the region. Describe how you made your choice, and provide evidence to support your decision. Hint: Sulfur dioxide, the main culprit in acid rain, is produced primarily by power plants that burn fossil fuels. Sulfur dioxide mixes with air. It takes time to form sulfuric acid, so the acid rain is likely to fall some distance from the sulfur dioxide source.

_____

_____

_____

_____

_____

_____

INVESTIGATION

6.2

THE ACID TEST

Acid precipitation is one of the effects of air pollution. When nitrogen- or sulfur-containing pollutants react with water vapor in clouds, dilute acids form. These acids fall to the Earth as acid precipitation.

Often, acid precipitation does not occur in the same place where the pollutants are released. The acid precipitation usually falls some distance downwind—sometimes hundreds of kilometers away. Thus, the site that causes acid precipitation may not suffer its effects. This is one of the reasons why solving the problem of acid precipitation has been so difficult.

Coal-burning power plants are one source of air pollution. These power plants release the chemical sulfur dioxide into the air. Sulfur dioxide reacts chemically with the water vapor in air to produce sulfur-containing acids, which later fall to Earth as acid precipitation.

In this Investigation you will perform a chemical reaction that produces sulfur dioxide. When this sulfur dioxide reacts with water vapor in the air, the same acids that result from coal-burning power plants form. You will observe the effects of these acids on plants.

MATERIALS

- 2 g sodium nitrite
- 2 mL sulfuric acid (1 M)
- 2 potted houseplants of the same type (impatiens, marigolds, and pansies are good choices)
- 2 large, clear plastic bags
- 50 mL beaker
- twist tie or tape

PROCEDURE

1. Place 2 g of sodium nitrite in a beaker. Place a plant and the beaker inside the plastic bag. Do not seal the bag yet.

   Caution: Steps 2–4 should be carried out ONLY under a fume hood or outdoors.

2. Carefully add 2 mL of a 1 M solution of sulfuric acid to the beaker. Immediately seal the bag tightly, and secure the seal with a twist tie or tape. *Caution: Because this reaction produces sulfur dioxide, a toxic gas, the bag should be absolutely free of leaks. If a leak occurs, move away from the bag until the reaction is complete and the gas has dissipated.*

3. Seal an identical plant in an identical bag that does not contain sodium nitrite or sulfuric acid.

4. After 10 minutes, cut both bags open. Stay at least 5 m away from the bags as the sulfur dioxide gas dissipates. Keep the plants and bags in the fume hood.

5. Predict the effects of the experiment on each plant over the next few days. Record your predictions.

_____

_____

6. Observe both plants over the next 3 days. Record your observations below.

Day	Control plant	Experimental plant
1		
2		
3		

ANALYZE

7. What does this experiment suggest about the effects of acid precipitation on vegetation?

_____

8. a. In what ways is this experiment a realistic simulation of acid precipitation?

_____

_____

b. In what ways is this experiment NOT a realistic simulation?

_____

_____

_____

_____

9. Would you expect to see similar effects occur as rapidly, more rapidly, or less rapidly in real life? Explain.

_____

_____

_____

INVESTIGATION 7.1

BUILD A MODEL OF GLOBAL AIR MOVEMENT

Warm air rises and cools, and cold air sinks and warms. This is true whether we are observing the temperature and air circulation in a room or around the globe. On Earth this movement of air creates a system of wind currents that you will demonstrate by building a model. You will build a closed system in which ice simulates the polar regions and a lamp simulates the equator. You will follow the movement of air over these regions by watching a trail of smoke as it traces the path of air.

SET UP YOUR GLOBAL MODEL

1. Stack the ice cubes on the bottom and against one end of the aquarium. Place the lamp outside the other end of the aquarium with the bulb directed at the bottom half of that end. Use masking tape to attach one thermometer to each end inside of the aquarium. Make sure the thermometers can be read from the outside of the tank. Place the cover on the aquarium.

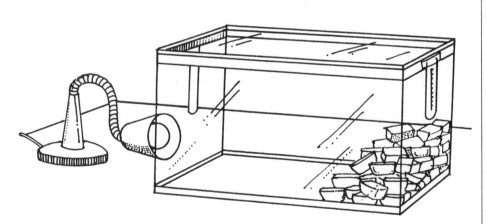

2. Wait 5 minutes; then read and record the temperature at each end of the aquarium.

_____

3. Light the end of the incense stick so that it produces a steady plume of smoke.

4. Lift the aquarium cover very slightly so that you can insert the incense stick. Hold it steadily in place over the ice about 5 cm from the cover.

MATERIALS

- 15 gal. glass aquarium with cover
- 2 outdoor thermometers
- adjustable goose-neck lamp with a 100 W incandescent bulb
- masking tape
- 24 large ice cubes
- incense stick
- matches

OBSERVE AND RECORD

5. How does the smoke behave? Draw a diagram of the aquarium. Use arrows to indicate the movement of the smoke.

6. Why is the difference between temperatures at the two ends of the aquarium an important factor in the flow of heat through the aquarium?

_____

_____

_____

7. Remove several ice cubes. Does the air movement pattern change when some ice is removed? Why?

_____

_____

_____

APPLY WHAT YOU HAVE LEARNED

8. A *closed system* is a collection of elements that nothing can escape from or enter. Your aquarium is an example of a (practically) closed system. *Convection* is the movement of warm air relative to cooler air. Discuss your observations of convection in the closed system of the aquarium. How can you apply this information to the movement of air over the Earth?

_____

_____

_____

_____

_____

_____

_____

_____

_____

_____

9. Predict how air movement patterns might change if polar ice began to thaw due to global warming.

_____

_____

_____

_____

_____

_____

_____

_____

_____

_____

_____

10. How is the Earth and its atmosphere like the closed system of your aquarium model? What factors exist on Earth but not in your model that affect air movement, climate, and weather?

_____

_____

_____

_____

_____

_____

_____

_____

_____

_____

Name_____ Class_____ Date_____

METHYL BROMIDE:
THE OZONE'S ENEMY

MATERIALS
- graph paper
- colored pens or pencils

A layer of ozone is located in the stratosphere, more than 7 mi. above the Earth's surface. In section 7-4 you learned about ozone's protective function and about the chemicals called CFCs that damage this layer.

Methyl bromide, a chemical byproduct of the production of fire-retarding materials for the electronics industry, destroys the ozone layer. Methyl bromide kills organisms such as insects, nematodes, weeds, and rodents; and it causes respiratory and central nervous system problems in humans. It is commonly used as a pesticide in soil where strawberries and tomatoes are grown in Florida and California. As much as 95 percent of methyl bromide eventually enters the atmosphere, where it damages ozone.

Scientists use an index called the ozone depletion potential (ODP) to compare a substance's ability to destroy ozone. CFCs have ODPs that range from 0.1 to 1. Substances with higher numbers have more destructive potential. Methyl bromide has an ODP of 0.6. The Clean Air Act requires the phasing out of all substances with an ozone depletion potential of 0.2 or greater, including methyl bromide, by the year 2001. In addition, the Montreal Protocol, an international treaty to protect the earth's atmosphere, lists methyl bromide as a chemical concern.

ANALYZE THE DATA

The chart on the next page shows the level of worldwide production of methyl bromide and the changing thickness of the ozone layer between the years 1979 and 1994. The thickness of the ozone layer is measured in Dobson units. The ozone layer as it exists in the stratosphere is several kilometers thick due to the low pressure at that distance above the Earth's surface. But if you were to bring the ozone layer to the Earth's surface, the pressure would compress it to only 0.3 cm thick. To standardize comparisons of the ozone layer's thickness, the Dobson unit is defined as 0.001 atm-cm.

1. What was happening to the ozone layer in the years before methyl bromide began to be produced?

_____

2. Can you think of a possible explanation for the change in the thickness of the ozone layer in the years before methyl bromide was produced?

_____

_____

_____

Methyl Bromide and Ozone Data		
Year	Metric tons sold	Dobson units
1979	0	209
1980	0	205
1981	0	205
1982	0	189
1983	0	169
1984	100,468	154
1985	106,423	146
1986	111,233	159
1987	122,774	120
1988	133,621	173
1989	137,942	124
1990	146,923	128
1991	162,259	117
1992	157,816	124
1993	160,181	94
1994	162,547	88

GRAPH THE DATA

3. On a piece of graph paper plot the data from the chart above. Put the years on the x-axis and metric tons of methyl bromide sold on the y-axis. Label the y-axis in increments of 5,000. Connect these points smoothly using a best-fit line. On the same graph create a second vertical y-axis on the right. Label it with Dobson units with values from 80 to 200 in increments of 10. Graph the ozone layer data. Make this y-axis a curving best-fit line in a different color.

4. Does the increased use of methyl bromide correlate with the decrease of the ozone layer?

_____

_____

_____

5. If there is a correlation, does that prove that methyl bromide causes ozone destruction?

_____

_____

INVESTIGATION 7.3

HOW EFFECTIVE ARE SUNSCREENS?

It's a gorgeous summer day, and you plan to spend the day swimming and soaking up some rays at a nearby park. Not wanting to suffer a painful burn, you grab a hat, spread a layer of sunscreen over your exposed skin, and put on some sunglasses before you leave.

You may know that it is the sun's ultraviolet (UV) rays that can burn you. Sunglasses and a hat provide shade for your eyes and face, but how does sunscreen help protect you?

Many sunscreens contain a chemical called para-aminobenzoic acid (PABA), which absorbs UV rays before they can be absorbed by your skin. Sunscreens use a numbered rating system. According to this system, the higher the number, the higher the concentration of PABA and the greater the UV absorption. For example, if your sunscreen has an SPF (sun protection factor) of 8, you can theoretically stay in the sun eight times longer than you could with no protection. That is, the sunscreen reduces the amount of UV radiation that your skin absorbs by a factor of 8.

Do sunscreens *really* protect us against UV radiation? Does the rating system *really* give us a way to judge the relative strength of different sunscreens? Conduct the following experiment to find out.

MATERIALS

- water
- 4 sunscreen lotions with different SPF ratings
- suntan lotion containing no sunscreen (such as baby oil)
- sheet of sun-sensitive paper
- 5 small acrylic sheets, about 3 cm × 5 cm
- 5 cotton swabs
- wax pencil
- several sheets of dark construction paper or a dark cloth
- baking sheet

SUNNY SIDE UP

1. Use a wax pencil to label each acrylic sheet with the SPF rating of one of the lotions you will be testing. Include the lotion with no sunscreen.

2. Place a drop of each grade of lotion on the corresponding acrylic sheet. Using a clean cotton swab for each sample, evenly spread the lotion over the surface of each sheet.

3. Working rapidly, place a piece of sun-sensitive paper on a baking sheet with the blue side up. Arrange the acrylic sheets (lotion side up) on the paper from lowest to highest SPF. Label the paper to show the SPF of each acrylic sheet. Quickly cover the tray and sheets with dark paper to avoid exposure to light.

4. Carry the tray outside to a sunny location and uncover it, exposing it to the sun. The blue paper will fade to very light blue. This process may take up to 15 minutes, depending on solar intensity. Watch carefully as the paper fades. As soon as the paper around the acrylic sheets fades completely, cover the tray and take it back to your classroom.

5. Remove the cover and acrylic sheets from the paper. Rinse the sun-sensitive paper in cold water for one minute and spread it flat to dry.

6. Allow the sun-sensitive paper to dry, and then examine the spots where the acrylic sheets were placed.

ANALYSIS

7. a. Describe your results.

_____

_____

b. Which lotion offered the most protection? _____ the least? _____

c. Is there a noticeable difference in protection from one SPF rating to the next?

_____

_____

8. Which lotion would you recommend to someone who anticipates being in the sun for a long period of time? Why?

_____

_____

_____

_____

9. What variables could have affected your results?

_____

_____

_____

_____

10. Which lotion was the control in this experiment?

_____

11. How might you change this experiment to better control your variables?

_____

_____

_____

GOING FURTHER

12. Collect sunglasses and test their degree of UV protection by placing the lenses on sheets of sun-sensitive paper and conducting the experiment again.

I N V E S T I G A T I O N

8.1

CHANGING LANDSCAPES

How has the landscape of your area changed over time? The landscape of the United States has changed dramatically as land use has changed. *Land use* refers to how humans use land, such as for farming, industry, recreation, or housing.

One aspect of the landscape that changes through land use is *land cover*—the natural plant communities, such as forest and grassland, that exist in a given area. The number of people per unit land area is called *population density*. Land cover is usually capable of absorbing the effects of low-density human populations. The population of the continental United States has greatly increased in the last few decades, while the land area has stayed the same.

In this Investigation, you will determine the extent of local landscape changes by studying aerial photographs and maps of your area. As part of a land-use planning group, you will create a land use map to evaluate changes in the landscape. Keep your pencils sharp—and your eyes sharper.

MATERIALS

- highlighter pen
- metric ruler
- calculator
- magnifying lens
- transparency grids
- colored pencils
- USGS quadrangle map*
- 2 aerial photos*

EXAMINE THE LAY OF THE LAND

1. Your teacher will provide you with a United States Geological Survey (USGS) quadrangle map that includes the study area. Examine the map closely. What types of land use in the study area are apparent from the map?

   _____

   _____

   _____

   _____

2. Look carefully at the two aerial photos of this area. One is a recent shot, and the other is an older aerial photo of the area. These photos may be at different scales, so features may look larger or smaller. Are there any other obvious differences between the photos? What changes in the landscape do you notice?

   _____

   _____

   _____

   _____

3. Locate any populated areas in the older photograph. Use a magnifying lens to pick out buildings. Buildings cast a shadow, so look for a white/black pattern. Are the buildings placed close together, or are they spread out over the study area? Is the current populated area urban? If not, what is it?

_____

_____

_____

_____

4. Notice whether there are any dark areas in the older photo. Dark areas are usually wooded areas, such as pine forests. Compare any forest cover in the older photo with that in the recent photo. How has the forest cover changed?

_____

_____

_____

_____

5. Find evidence of non-forested plant cover in the older photo. Cropland usually appears as uniform rectangles or circles, while rangeland and grassland appears with more texture and less-precise borders. How has the non-forested plant cover changed in the recent photo? What do you think might account for these changes?

_____

_____

_____

_____

6. Look for barren areas—places where soil and rock are exposed—in the original photo. Is there evidence of erosion? Are there any new barren areas in the recent photo? If so, do you think these changes are the result of human activity or natural processes?

_____

_____

_____

_____

INVESTIGATION 8.1, CONTINUED

MAP THE STUDY AREA

7. Place a transparency grid over the original photo, and trace the study area on the transparency. Trace the borders of the areas of different land use, and fill in each area with a different color. You have just created a land use map! Do the same for the recent photo.

8. Count the graph squares within each land-use border on your map, and write the number in the table below. Calculate the percentage of the total land area devoted to each land-use type, and write this data in the "Original photo" column in the chart below. Repeat this step for the recent photo.

Study Area Data Collection Table

Original photo			Recent photo		
Land-use type	Number of squares	Percent	**Land-use type**	Number of squares	Percent
Urban/suburban			Urban/suburban		
Cropland			Cropland		
Rangeland/grassland			Rangeland/grassland		
Forested land			Forested land		
Water bodies			Water bodies		
Wetland			Wetland		
Exposed soil and rock			Exposed soil and rock		
Total		100%	Total		100%

9. Use the data above to complete the pie charts below.

Original Land-Use

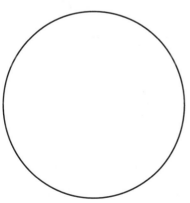

Recent Land-Use

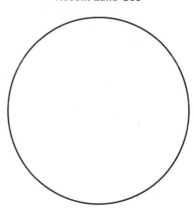

ANALYZE THE CHANGING LANDSCAPE

10. Has the overall land cover changed since the original photo was taken? Explain what might account for these changes.

_____

_____

_____

_____

11. Has the total area devoted to urban and suburban land use increased since the original photo was taken? If so, what other type(s) of land use and land cover have diminished?

_____

_____

_____

_____

12. Given what you have learned about land use trends in the study area, how do you think the land will change in the next 20 years? Explain your answer.

_____

_____

_____

_____

13. Think about how the anticipated changes in land use will affect the land cover of the study area. As a member of a local planning group, what recommendations would you make regarding future land use in the study area?

_____

_____

_____

_____

INVESTIGATION 9.1

MANAGING THE MOISTURE IN GARDEN SOIL

You work as a soil specialist with the Bucolic County Soil Conservation District. One day, you receive the following letter from a local resident.

LN.

Dear Sir or Madam,

My family recently started a small organic vegetable garden in our backyard in hopes of growing cheaper, fresher, and more healthful food than we can buy at the store. Unfortunately, we find that we must water our garden very often to keep it healthy, and our water bills are skyrocketing. What can we do to reduce the amount of water our garden needs? If the high water bills continue, we may have to give up this "money-saving" project.

Sincerely,

Latisha Norton

Mrs. Latisha Norton

MATERIALS
- soil sample
- metric balance
- crucible (or other heat-safe container)
- tongs
- heat source (Bunsen burner, hot plate, or oven)
- stirring rod
- funnel
- filter paper
- water
- eyedropper
- 250 mL beaker or cup
- watch (or clock)
- at least three of the following: chopped leaves; chopped sphagnum moss; decayed wood fiber; sawdust; flour; compost; cow manure; chopped grass clippings; Terrasorb® granules; other materials

When you read Mrs. Norton's letter, you realize that a likely problem is that water drains out of her garden soil too quickly. In order to give Mrs. Norton advice on how to improve her soil, you want to find out how much water it can hold. After calling to discuss the situation, you visit her garden and collect several soil samples.

1. Dry your soil sample without burning organic matter. To do this, place about 50 g of soil in a crucible or other heat-safe container. Using tongs, gently heat it over a Bunsen burner or hot plate or put it in an oven. Stir the sample occasionally with a stirring rod to ensure complete drying.

2. After the sample is completely dry, weigh out about 10 g of dry soil. Record its exact mass in the table on the next page.

3. Dampen a circle of filter paper until it is thoroughly moist, but not dripping. Weigh the moist filter paper, and record its mass in the table.

4. Fold the filter paper into quarters, and then open it as shown in the illustration to form a "cup" that fits in a funnel. Place the filter paper in the funnel.

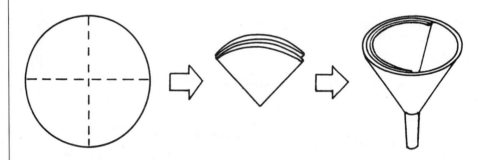

5. Place the dry soil sample on the filter paper in the funnel. Place the funnel in a small beaker or cup.

6. Add water to the soil sample one drop at a time until all of the soil is moist and water begins to drip out of the funnel. Stop adding water, and set the funnel aside for 5 minutes.

7. After 5 minutes, remove the filter paper and moist soil from the funnel, and weigh them together. Record their mass in the table.

8. Calculate the mass of the moistened soil sample (**D**) by subtracting the mass of the damp filter paper (**B**) from the mass of the completely moistened sample with filter paper (**C**). Record the result in the table.

9. Calculate the amount of water that your soil sample can hold (**E**) by subtracting the mass of the dry soil sample (**A**) from the mass of the moistened soil sample (**D**). Record the result in the table.

10. Calculate the percent water-holding capacity of your sample (**F**) by dividing the mass of water held (**E**) by the mass of the moistened soil sample (**D**) and multiplying by 100. The higher the percent water-holding capacity, the more water the soil can hold. Record the result in the table.

	A Mass of dry soil	B Mass of damp filter paper	C Mass of moistened sample with filter paper	D Mass of moistened sample (C–B)	E Mass of water held (D–A)	F Percent water- holding capacity (E/D)×100
Unmodified sample						
Sample mixed with: _____						
Sample mixed with: _____						
Sample mixed with: _____						

11. Compare your results with those of your classmates, or perform the same test on different samples. Which soil sample had the best water-holding capacity? Why do you think this is so?

_____

_____

_____

12. Divide the remaining dry soil sample into three 5 g portions. To each portion, add 5 g of any one of the following materials: chopped dry leaves; chopped dry sphagnum moss; dry decayed wood fiber; sawdust; flour; dry compost; dry cow manure; dry chopped grass clippings; Terrasorb® granules; or other materials that you bring or are provided by your teacher. Make sure that any material you use is thoroughly dry before blending it with the soil. Weigh each mixed soil sample, and record the masses in the table on the previous page.

13. Perform steps 3 through 10 for your mixed soil samples. Record your results in the table.

14. Which additive improved the soil's water-holding capacity the most? Why do you think this is so?

_____

_____

_____

_____

_____

15. Based on your experimental results as well as your reading on this subject, what could you recommend to Mrs. Norton to reduce the amount of water her garden needs?

_____

_____

_____

_____

INVESTIGATION 9.2

MODELING PESTICIDE POLLUTION

Congratulations! You've just been hired by the Fluterton County Water Safety Service as director of field research. Your first assignment is to respond to the following letter from a concerned resident of the county.

MATERIALS

- bottom two-thirds of a clear, 2 L soda bottle
- light-colored sand
- light-colored aquarium gravel
- piece of nylon stocking
- small rubber band
- spray nozzle and tube from a spray bottle
- red food coloring
- blue watercolor paint in solid form
- 500 mL beaker
- paper cup
- water

Director of Field Research
Fluterton County
Water Safety Service
P.O. Box 3001
Fluterton, IL 61807

Dear Sir or Madam:

We recently had our well water tested for the first time in a few years. When the results came back, they showed contaminants that were not there before: trace amounts of a pesticide that was used many years ago on some nearby farms, as well as small amounts of several petroleum products. First of all, how could a pesticide that was used 20 years ago suddenly affect our water today? Also, we've noticed that the litter problem around here has been getting pretty bad lately. Is that going to contaminate our water too? If so, when? As you might imagine, we are more than a little concerned.

Sincerely,

Tracey Watson

Tracey Watson

In the course of your research, you find the following passage in a water safety journal:

> In the United States, about one-fifth of our fresh water comes from underground sources. Homes that rely on wells are just one example of groundwater use. Wells are drilled down to where the ground is saturated, and the water stored there is pumped up to the surface. Aquifers and other groundwater sources are replenished gradually by surface water that seeps down through the soil; unfortunately, this water can often contain particulates, dissolved chemicals, and other substances that contaminate the groundwater.

Building a model of a well will allow you to address Ms. Watson's concerns. With your model, you will not only investigate the process by which groundwater sources become polluted, but also see how different types of pollution from the surface can eventually end up in well water.

BUILD A WELL

1. Fill the soda bottle about half full with aquarium gravel.

2. Fold the piece of nylon stocking several times, and place it across the open end of the sprayer tube. Secure it tightly with the rubber band. Insert the tube into the gravel along the side of the bottle—the end of the tube should be about 3 cm from the bottom.

3. Add water until it just covers the gravel. Then add sand to about 3 cm from the top of the bottle. Pump the nozzle a few times to get the flow of water started. Spray the water into the beaker.

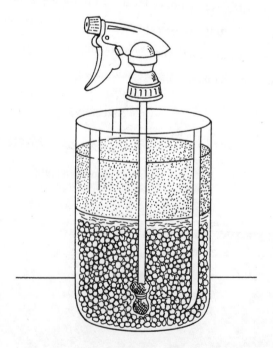

4. Pump the nozzle and observe the water level in the soda bottle. What happens?

_____

_____

_____

5. With your pencil, punch a few small holes in the bottom of the paper cup. To simulate precipitation, fill the cup with water and let the water drizzle out through the holes onto the sand. Try to avoid stirring up the sand, because this may cause the sand to seep down and clog the tube. Practice adding precipitation while you pump the well until you can add and remove water at about the same rate.

ADD SOME POLLUTION

6. Place 10 drops of red food coloring on top of the sand. This represents pollution, such as pesticides or other chemicals, that is dissolved in surface runoff. Begin pumping the well and adding precipitation. As you proceed, be sure that the water level stays between the surface of the sand and the end of the tube. Watch for red coloration to appear in your discharge beaker. How many squeezes of the trigger does it take for the food coloring to pass through the well?

_____

7. Is your well polluted permanently? Explain.

_____

_____

_____

8. Place a few crumbled bits of blue paint on top of the sand. This represents waste or other solid pollutants that contaminate groundwater by dissolving in surface water that seeps into the ground. Repeat the process described in step 6. How many squeezes does it take for the color to appear this time?

_____

9. Explain why the food coloring passed through the well at a different rate than did the crumbled paint.

_____

_____

_____

10. Explain how a different rate of precipitation would affect the speed at which a pollutant shows up in the pumped water.

_____

_____

_____

RESPOND TO THE PUBLIC'S CONCERNS

11. In Ms. Watson's letter, she asked: "How could a pesticide used 20 years ago suddenly affect our water today?" Using what you've learned about ground-water pollution, how would you answer this question?

_____

_____

_____

_____

_____

12. She also asked if the growing litter problem in the area could affect her water supply. Do you think this is a valid concern? Explain.

_____

_____

_____

13. From the rates at which a liquid (the food coloring) and a solid (the paint) passed through your well, you can establish a ratio of the liquid rate to the solid rate. Assuming for the moment that this ratio applies to all types of liquids and solids, calculate how long it will take for the litter problem to affect Ms. Watson's water supply.

_____

_____

_____

_____

INVESTIGATION 9.3

WHICH CROPS TOLERATE SALT?

County of Dixon
Road Services Extension Office

Dear extension officers:
Every year, we have significant snowfall and ice on our roads. I appreciate your efforts to make the roads safe for travel, but every spring I become concerned about the damage done by this road clearing. In particular, I am worried that the salt used to melt snow and ice harms the crops we have planted near Route 4. I wonder if you could tell me which kinds of crop plants can best tolerate the yearly accumulation of salt. Thanks for your help.

Yours truly,

Joan Smith

When Joan Smith's letter arrives at the county office, Extension Officer Tom Watts is curious. He's not aware of any especially salt-tolerant crops, so he decides to use this question as the basis for an investigation. He decides the best way to find plants that tolerate salt is to raise seeds from different plants using different concentrations of salt-water solutions and find out which seeds survive best.

MATERIALS

- table salt
- 1 gal. sealable plastic bags (4)
- measuring cup and spoon
- 3 L plastic bottles with caps (4)
- funnel
- paper towels
- stapler
- permanent marking pen
- plant seeds: alfalfa, clover, wild rye, wheat grass, and fescue
- small pots and soil (optional)

PROCEDURE

1. How could Tom state the problem he's investigating?

_____

2. First, make a very concentrated saltwater solution by mixing 300 g of table salt in 3 L of water. Store this solution in a sealed 3 L bottle for 24 hours. This is the "0% dilution"; it's not diluted at all.

3. Choose and prepare three dilutions of this standard solution. Use the table below to find out how much of the standard solution to mix with a given amount of fresh water for each dilution. For example, to make a 60 percent dilution, mix 200 mL of the standard solution with 300 mL of fresh water. Make sure to label each solution bottle.

Dilution Recipes		
Dilution	**Standard solution (control)**	**Fresh water**
0% (control)	500 mL	0 mL
10%	450 mL	50 mL
20%	400 mL	100 mL
30%	350 mL	150 mL
40%	300 mL	200 mL
50%	250 mL	250 mL
60%	200 mL	300 mL
70%	150 mL	350 mL
80%	100 mL	400 mL
90%	50 mL	450 mL
100%	0 mL	500 mL

4. List the dilutions you made below.

_____

5. Use the plastic sealable bags as germination chambers. You will need one bag for each salt dilution you plan to test. Cut or fold a paper towel and fit 2 to 4 layers flat inside each plastic bag.

6. Starting at the bottom of the bag, make a row of 10 evenly spaced seeds using one kind of seed. Use the marking pen to label this row on the plastic bag. Separate this row of seeds from the next row by stapling several staples across the width of the bag. The seeds should be visible through one side of the bag.

7. Repeat step 5 for the remaining flour seed types. Why is it important to put each seed type in a separate row?

_____

_____

8. Lightly moisten the entire paper towel with 15 mL of one dilution of saltwater and seal the bag. With the marking pen, label the bag with its saltwater dilution.

9. Repeat steps 5–8 for each saltwater dilution. Make sure that you use fresh water (100% dilution) for one bag of seeds. Why is it important to use fresh water in one bag of seeds?

_____

_____

10. Set aside each of the prepared dilutions. Place the bags out of direct sunlight and away from heat for 10 days. Water them daily with the same saltwater dilution initially used. After 10 days, record your observations in the data chart below.

Germination Success			
Seed type	Number of seeds planted	Number of seeds germinated	Percent germination (number germinated/ number planted)

11. Based on your results, what seeds can Tom Watts recommend for planting in salty areas?

_____

_____

_____

12. Alfalfa and clover develop a single main root, called a taproot, while fescue, wheat grass, and wild rye have branching root systems. Based on your results, is there a correlation between root type and salt tolerance?

_____

_____

_____

_____

13. Use the second data table below to summarize your class results.

Class Results for Germination Success				
Dilution (control)	Germination success by seed type			
0%				
10%				
20%				
30%				
40%				
50%				
60%				
70%				
80%				
90%				
100%				

14. Why is it important to know what percentage of the control group (100% dilution) germinated?

_____

_____

_____

_____

_____

_____

_____

15. What percentage of the control group germinated?

_____

_____

16. Which seeds are the most salt-tolerant? How can you tell?

_____

_____

_____

_____

_____

EXTENSION

Here is a method for doing a more comprehensive test of plants' salt tolerance. Start with the germinated seeds used in the Investigation. Transfer each row of seeds to a separate pot filled with peat, which is composed of decaying plant matter. Label each pot with the seed type and the dilution of the standard saltwater solution. Water all of the seeds with tap water that was left at room temperature overnight. Maintain the same light and temperature levels for all plants during the course of the experiment. Continue watering the seeds every other day with 15 mL of "aged" tap water. After 8 weeks, water the plants every other day with 5–10 mL of the same dilution that you indicated on the pots. Evaluate the effect of salt concentration by comparing the percentage of plants that survive at different concentrations.

I N V E S T I G A T I O N

10.1

DIVERSITY IN A DROP

Within any ecosystem, organisms form a complex web of physical, chemical, and biological interactions. The health of an ecosystem depends on the involvement of all of the organisms, whether they are producers, consumers, or decomposers. When any part of the web is disrupted or destroyed, the whole ecosystem suffers.

In this Investigation, you will study biodiversity in an aquatic environment. By altering the physical characteristics of your ecosystem, you will be able to see how biodiversity can be affected. From your results, you will infer the effects of physical changes on biodiversity in natural ecosystems.

INITIAL OBSERVATIONS

1. Obtain a sample of pond water. Swirl the water gently. Then use the eyedropper to place a drop or two on a microscope slide. Cover the drops with a coverslip. If you have too much water, use the corner of a paper towel to absorb the excess water.

2. Set the microscope to medium power, and examine your slide. (If you are unable to see organisms at first, try looking at other parts of the slide or preparing a new slide.) Locate bright green organisms; these are algae (producers). The green color comes from chlorophyll, a pigment that allows photosynthesis to occur. Also look for moving organisms; these are protozoa (unicellular consumers). They may be clear, brown, or slightly green (from having consumed algae). Then switch your microscope to its highest power. At the edge of a clump of algae, look for tiny wriggling forms; these are bacteria (decomposers in most cases). Using the space below, sketch and label all of the organisms that are visible on your microscope slide.

3. How is the role of the producers (the algae) in this ecosystem different from the role of the decomposers (the bacteria)?

_____

_____

_____

_____

_____

_____

MATERIALS

- microscope
- microscope slides with coverslips
- eyedropper
- pH paper
- pond water containing mud and algae
- 1 L clear container with a lid
- one of the following: 10 mL bleach, 10 mL vinegar, or 1 g fertilizer
- funnel
- paper towel
- stirring rod

ALTERING THE ECOSYSTEM

4. Test the pH of the sample. State the pH and indicate whether it is acidic, neutral, or basic.

_____

_____

5. Carefully read each of the following procedures for altering the ecosystem, and pick one to carry out.

Procedure A: Transfer approximately 400 mL of your sample to a sealed container. Be sure to include algae and a small amount of mud. Place the container in a cool, dark location for 3 to 5 days.

Procedure B: Transfer approximately 800 mL of your sample to an open, clear container. Add 1 g of houseplant fertilizer to the sample, and swirl the water gently to dissolve the fertilizer. Place the container in a location that receives direct sunlight for 3 to 5 days.

Procedure C: Transfer approximately 600 mL of your sample to an open, clear container. Add 10 mL of household bleach (a base), and place the container in a location that receives indirect sunlight for 1 to 2 days.

Procedure D: Transfer approximately 600 mL of your sample to an open, clear container. Add 10 mL of household vinegar (an acid), and place the container in a location that receives indirect sunlight for 1 to 2 days.

Which procedure did you choose? _____

6. Each of the above procedures involves a physical and/or chemical change to the ecosystem. What do you predict will happen to the biodiversity of your ecosystem when you carry out your chosen procedure?

_____

_____

_____

7. Carry out the procedure you have chosen. Be sure to label your container with your names and the letter of procedure.

ANALYZING THE RESULTS

8. After the appropriate number of days have passed, prepare a microscope slide of the sample as you did earlier. Examine the slide under the microscope. Test the pH of the water in the sample. Compare your findings with your initial observations. What differences do you observe?

_____

_____

_____

_____

_____

_____

_____

9. How has the biodiversity of organisms in the ecosystem changed?

_____

_____

_____

10. Did the different types of organisms in the ecosystem show different degrees of sensitivity to the changes in their environment? Explain.

_____

_____

_____

_____

11. Discuss your results with students who followed different procedures. Which of the four procedures do you think was the most destructive to the ecosystem? Explain your answer.

_____

_____

_____

_____

_____

12. So far, only short-term effects of changes to the physical and chemical characteristics of an environment have been discussed. Imagine that a change similar to **Procedure B** (artificial eutrophication) occurred in a pond in a wilderness area. What would be the long-term effects of this change?

_____

_____

_____

_____

_____

_____

13. Why must the management of an ecosystem take into account the need for biological diversity?

_____

_____

_____

_____

_____

_____

_____

_____

_____

I N V E S T I G A T I O N

10.2

DESIGNING A PRESERVE

The organisms alive today are the products of millions of years of evolutionary history and can never be replaced if they are lost. Yet much of the Earth's biodiversity is seriously threatened. Scientists estimate that nearly 20 percent of all species will become extinct in the next half century if current trends continue. Concerned people are trying to devise ways to save as many species as possible. Zoos, seed banks, botanical gardens, and arboreta are part of the solution. However, most species cannot be sustained for long outside their native ecosystems. For this reason, scientists believe it is crucial to set aside protected areas, or *nature preserves,* where species can live undisturbed by human development.

A successful preserve requires careful planning. Size and shape are the most important considerations. A preserve should be large enough to sustain a healthy population of many different species, including those at the top of food chains. It should also encompass a variety of ecosystem types—such as grassland, forest, and wetland—so that it protects a broad range of species. However, if it is possible to preserve only a relatively small area, it may be more important to protect as much of the rarest ecosystem as possible. Preserve designers must balance all of these considerations. In this Investigation, you will design a preserve "in your own backyard"—that is, in the area surrounding your hometown.

MATERIALS

- tracing paper
- colored pencils
- metric ruler
- topographic map
- field guides of local animals and plants

EVALUATE YOUR ECOSYSTEM

1. Brainstorm about one or more ecosystems in your area that are threatened by human development.

_____

2. On tracing paper, use your ruler to create a 16 cm × 20 cm rectangle for a total area of 320 cm². This will be the size of the area you can consider in deciding where to locate your preserve. Divide this rectangle into 20 subdivisions, or *quadrates.* Each quadrate should be 4 cm × 4 cm (16 cm²).

3. Examine the topographic map. Place your tracing paper over a natural area that is next to at least one town, and that includes several kinds of ecosystems. Trace the topographic contour lines with black pencil, and the streams and lakes with blue pencil. Lightly shade different ecosystem types with different colors, and trace roads and other human-built infrastructures. Be consistent with your symbols and colors so that similar features are coded the same way.

4. Think about the plants and animals that are likely to live in the area you have traced. Consult field guides for information on the habitat requirements of different species. Next, refer to the energy pyramid on page 61 of the textbook, and select two or more representative species for each of four trophic levels. These species will represent the local biodiversity.

5. Look again at the topographic map. It should have a map key along the bottom. Create a key on your tracing paper in the bottom left-hand corner. Include the scale the map is drawn to as well as labeled symbols for the features you have included. Next include the organisms you chose in step 4. Write the common species name followed by the scientific name. Then draw a symbol representing that organism to the right of its scientific name. For example, a small red maple leaf could represent maple trees and a black mask could represent raccoons.

6. Determine how many individuals of each species would probably live in the area you have chosen. In your field guide, look up the habitat requirements, or range, of the top carnivores you have chosen. Then use the 10× rule expressed in the energy pyramid to determine reasonable numbers for species on lower trophic levels. To the right of each organism's symbol, write the number of individuals represented by that symbol. For instance, one maple leaf could represent 25 maple trees.

Species in My Area			
Plant species name	Estimated number	Animal species name	Estimated number

7. Draw your species symbols in places where the species are most likely to occur. Again, remember that the total number of individual plants should be about 10 times larger that the total number of primary consumers, and so on, up the food chain.

PLAN YOUR PRESERVE

8. Imagine that your town government and a local developer are going to build homes, shopping malls, roads, and other infrastructure on 80 percent of your traced area. They will set aside 20 percent of the area as a nature preserve. They have hired you to plan the size and shape of this preserve. Calculate how large an area you can preserve in terms of quadrates, and write your answer below.

_____

9. You decide to preserve as much biodiversity as possible. But how does one measure biodiversity? Scientists use several indicators to estimate the diversity of species living in an area. One indicator is *species richness,* the number of species present in a given area. Determine the species richness of each quadrate by counting the number of species present. For example, if there are five species in a given quadrate, then the species richness is 5. Another indicator of biodiversity is the number of trophic levels present, or the *trophic level richness.* Refer to pages 60 and 61 of your textbook to review the concept of trophic levels. Determine the trophic level richness by determining how many trophic levels there are among the species in your community. For example, if a quadrate contains plants, crickets, and toads, then the quadrate contains 3 trophic levels. Tally the organisms present in each quadrate, and record the species richness and trophic level richness in the chart below.

Indicators of Species Diversity										
Quadrate	1	2	3	4	5	6	7	8	9	10
Species richness										
Trophic level richness										
Quadrate	11	12	13	14	15	16	17	18	19	20
Species richness										
Trophic level richness										

10. Which quadrate has:

the most species richness?_____

the most trophic level richness?_____

11. Although your preserve must be four quadrates in size, its boundaries do not have to correspond to quadrate boundaries. In other words, your preserve can be whatever shape you want. Explain where you intend to locate your preserve, and justify your decision.

_____

_____

_____

_____

12. Draw the boundary of your preserve on your map.

13. Does your preserve protect all of the species that you chose in step 4?

_____

14. Why do some areas contain more species than other areas? Think about what determines where species live.

_____

_____

_____

_____

15. The diversity of species living in an area, called *species-level diversity,* is the most commonly used measure of biodiversity, but it is by no means the only one. Scientists also refer to *habitat-level diversity* and *population-level diversity,* among others. What do you think scientists mean by habitat-level diversity? Why might scientists look at biodiversity from perspectives other than at the species level? Provide at least one example to support your viewpoint.

_____

_____

_____

_____

_____

_____

_____

I N V E S T I G A T I O N

11.1

WHICH IS THE BEST INSULATOR?

When winter temperatures plummet, how do you stay warm? You put on a sweater or a coat, or maybe both. The colder it gets, the more layers you wear. But do you know how these layers keep you warm?

Each layer traps small pockets of air. Air transfers heat very slowly. The transfer of heat from one material to another is called **conduction.** Materials that transfer heat rapidly are called conductors, and those that transfer heat slowly are called insulators. Air, therefore, is a very poor conductor of heat, making it a good insulator. One disadvantage to insulating with air is that air molecules tend to flow in currents, increasing the rate of heat transfer from the air to other materials.

Now you can understand why you wear many layers of clothing when it's cold—so you are enveloped in an insulator that keeps the heat close to your body.

In this activity, you and your partners will test the insulating qualities of various materials. First you will build a device for testing these materials and then you will evaluate the materials' effectiveness using your device.

TEST THE INSULATORS

1. Assemble an insulation tester like the one shown at right. Punch a hole for the thermometer through the center of the plastic lid with the nail.

2. Choose an insulating material to test and use it to fill the space between the inner and the outer containers of your insulation tester. On a separate sheet of paper, draw one diagram indicating the movement of heat if the material is a good insulator and another diagram indicating the movement of heat if the material is a poor insulator. Indicate the movement of heat with arrows.

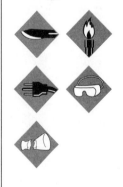

3. Make a table in your notebook to collect temperature data for each insulator. You will note the water temperature every 5 minutes over a 30-minute period.

MATERIALS

- coffee can with lid
- smaller can
- nail
- graduated cylinder
- saucepan or kettle
- heatproof mitt
- outdoor thermometer
- hot plate
- water
- various materials, such as sand, shredded paper, cardboard, sawdust, thick cloth, shredded plastic foam, cotton batting, feathers, wool, vermiculite, rock wool insulation, cellulose insulation, rigid foam insulation, or fiberglass insulation

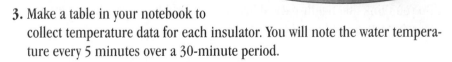

4. Measure 200 mL of water into a saucepan or kettle. Heat the water on the hot plate until it boils. Wearing the heatproof mitt, pour the water into the inner can. Do not wet the insulation or your results may be affected. **Caution:** *Be careful not to spill hot water on yourself or others.*

5. Quickly snap the plastic lid into place, and insert the thermometer so that the bulb is immersed in the water but does not touch the bottom of the inner can. Immediately measure and record the temperature. Continue to take measurements for 30 minutes.

6. Repeat steps 4 and 5 for each insulator you test.

7. Graph the temperature decline associated with each of the various insulators.

8. Repeat this experiment without using any insulating material. Record the data in a table in your notebook. How effective is air alone as an insulator? If air is a poor conductor of heat, how can you explain your results?

_____

_____

9. If time permits, test other materials. Compare your results with those of your classmates. Which material insulated most effectively? least effectively? How was this effectiveness demonstrated?

_____

_____

_____

_____

10. Describe any common characteristics among the most effective insulating materials.

_____

_____

_____

11. Do you think that tightly packed insulation would be more effective than loosely packed insulation? Why or why not?

_____

_____

INVESTIGATION 11.2

SMOKESTACK IN A BOTTLE

Combustion is a kind of chemical change in which chemical substances are burned to produce energy. Fuels that we burn to warm our homes, generate electricity, or do other useful work are made primarily of carbon, hydrogen, nitrogen, and oxygen. When they *combust,* or burn, these chemicals combine with oxygen and are transformed into new substances. Although some of the products of combustion are invisible to us, their presence in the air contributes to global warming and air pollution. Other combustion products, such as soot, may visibly contribute to the pollution problem. In this laboratory activity, you will use a candle to construct a model of a smokestack in order to study the products of combustion.

MATERIALS

- 1 gal. glass jar with screw-on lid
- limewater
- candle, 4–6 in. long
- matches
- clay
- metal spatula
- reference books

GETTING STARTED

1. With a small ball of clay, make a holder for your candle. Insert the candle in the holder and secure it to your work area so that it will not topple over. Then, light the candle.

BLACK SMOKE

2. Imagine that you are the engineer for a "smokestack" energy-producing facility (an energy plant that burns hydrocarbons for fuel). You have noticed that the smoke coming from your stack is blacker than usual. How can you find out where this black material is coming from and what you should do about it? Try some experiments to find out.

   a. Slowly bring the spatula into the orange portion of the candle flame, as shown below.

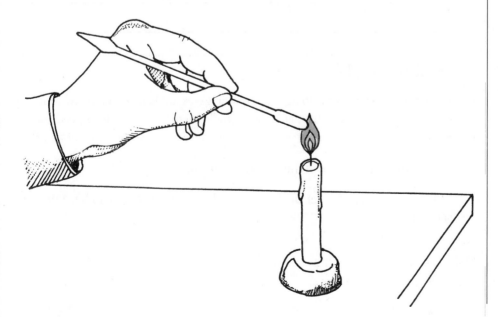

b. Describe what collects on the metal surface.

_____

_____

c. Where did this material come from? (Hint: What elements do all fuels contain?)

_____

_____

_____

d. Does the flame become "smoky" when you interfere with the incoming air around the flame by placing the spatula in its path?

_____

e. Blow out the candle.

f. Tiny particles suspended in the air are called particulates. They are one form of air pollution that increases the cost of keeping our clothes and furniture clean. More significantly, particulates can also cause health problems. Based on your experiments with the candle flame, what should you do to reduce the particulates given off by your smokestack?

_____

_____

_____

_____

_____

EMISSIONS TESTING

Part of your job as engineer is to determine what gases are being given off by your smokestack. To do so, you must place your "smokestack" (candle) in a sealed container and test the gases given off with a solution of calcium carbonate (limewater).

3. Secure your unlit candle in the bottom of the jar.

4. Light the candle, and cover the jar with the lid. Allow the candle to burn until it goes out.

5. Unscrew the lid, and remove the candle as quickly as possible. Pour about a half of an inch of limewater into the bottle. Replace the lid, and shake the contents.

a. What changes do you observe in the limewater?

_____

b. When limewater is exposed to carbon dioxide, small particles of calcium carbonate become suspended in the liquid, as you have just observed. What was the source of the carbon dioxide?

_____

_____

_____

_____

c. Although carbon dioxide is colorless and odorless, it is not a completely harmless gas in the atmosphere. What is the role of carbon dioxide in the warming of the Earth's atmosphere (global warming)?

_____

_____

_____

_____

HEAVY RAIN

Citizens living near the smokestack facility have been complaining that it rains more in their neighborhood than in other parts of the area. As engineer, you need to find out if any of the gases given off by your smokestack could be partly responsible for this.

6. Dispose of the mixture in the jar as your teacher directs. Carefully dry the inside of the jar, then place the candle back inside.

7. Light the candle, and screw on the lid as before. Carefully observe whether any moisture forms on the inside of the bottle.

a. Do you observe moisture forming in the bottle?

_____

b. Where could this moisture have come from? (Hint: Think about the elements involved in combustion.)

_____

_____

c. What will you tell the neighbors about the effect your smokestack has on the climate nearby?

_____

_____

_____

_____

EXTENSION

Another part of your job as engineer is to order new supplies of fuel. You learn about a supplier who can provide fuel at lower cost. However, this fuel is not as pure and contains more nitrogen and sulfur than the fuel you have been using. These elements will react with oxygen in air, giving rise to nitrogen oxides and sulfur oxides. To answer the following questions, you will need to do some research.

8. What effect do nitrogen oxides and sulfur oxides have on the atmosphere and the environment?

_____

_____

_____

_____

_____

_____

9. What factors must you consider in deciding whether or not to use the nitrogen- and sulfur-rich fuels?

_____

_____

_____

_____

I N V E S T I G A T I O N

12.1

SANITARY LANDFILLS VS. GARBAGE DUMPS

Garbage dumps used to be major eyesores and ecological nightmares. They smelled terrible, attracted scavengers, such as rats and seagulls, and oozed leachate into water supplies. However, in recent decades engineers have created more environmentally friendly facilities known as *sanitary landfills.* In sanitary landfills, liners prevent liquids from leaking into the soil and contaminating groundwater supplies, and alternating layers of waste and soil all but eliminate odors and scavengers. Some disposal operations even recycle, reuse, and compost organic material. But like most solutions to real-world problems, sanitary landfills have drawbacks, such as increased maintenance costs and space requirements. In this Investigation, you will build a model of a traditional garbage dump and of a modern landfill. You will then compare the two with respect to two important environmental considerations: the rate of decomposition and the amount of pollution produced.

MATERIALS

- 2 L plastic bottles (2)
- large nail
- 2 craft knives
- soil
- garbage items, such as food, paper, lawn clippings, paper clips, and plastic bags
- fine gravel or sand
- shallow pans
- spray bottle
- heat lamps
- small beaker
- colored pencils
- 12 in. thermometers (2)

BUILD MODEL LANDFILLS

1. Use the nail to punch holes in the sides and bottom of one bottle. Use the craft knife to carefully cut the tops from both bottles. Save the tops to use in step 3.

2. Place a thin layer of gravel or sand in the bottom of each container. You will need enough mixed garbage to fill each container half-way. In each container, alternate layers of trash and moistened soil to create three layers of each. Add an extra layer of soil on top to control odor and animal pests.

3. Make a few small slits in one of the bottle tops to reduce hazardous gas buildup during the experiment. Carefully tape the top back onto the hole-free bottle. Leave the other bottle open. You now have a model of the each type of landfill.

4. Place each bottle in a shallow pan, and place the setup in an area designated by your teacher.

5. Explain which bottle models a modern sanitary landfill.

_____

_____

6. Explain which bottle represents a traditional garbage dump.

_____

_____

THINK ABOUT IT

7. What landfill problems concern you most?

_____

_____

_____

_____

8. How might a landfill or its contents adversely affect the environment? How will you determine the environmental impact of each landfill model?

_____

_____

_____

_____

_____

OBSERVE CHANGES

For the rest of the experiment you will observe the decay of the materials in the two models and record your observations in the chart on the next page.

9. Switch off the heat lamp 24 hours before making your observations to ensure that the measured temperatures are due only to decomposition. Be careful moving the bottles. Draining leachate may stain clothes and have a foul odor.

10. Rate the changes in the look and smell of each bottle's contents on a scale of 1 to 5, with 1 indicating no change and 5 indicating complete decomposition. For example, if the waste looks unchanged, rate the contents a 1. Record the ratings in the table on the following page. Insert a thermometer through the opening of each bottle into the center of the landfills and wait 5 minutes. Measure and record the temperatures. Be sure to put the cap back on the closed landfill. Measure the volume of the leachate, and record your data in the table. Put the bottles back in the pan.

11. Dampen the soil in the open model with a spray bottle to keep the bacteria active, put the bottles back under the heat lamps, and switch on the lamps.

12. Repeat steps 9–11 once each week for 6 weeks to compare the levels of decay.

	Decay Look (1–5)		Decay Smell (1–5)		Decay Temp. (°C)		Pollution Leachate (in mL)		Brief description	
Week	Open	Closed	Open	Closed	Open	Closed	Open	Closed	Open	Closed
1										
2										
3										
4										
5										
6										

Decomposition Data

13. After 6 weeks, chart the temperature progression for each model on the middle graph below. Use blue for the open model and red for the closed model. What do you notice about the temperature changes in each model?

_____

14. Average the "look" and "smell" ratings for decay, and plot the averages for each week on the left-hand graph below. Use blue and red pencil as you did in step 13. Plot the cumulative volume of leachate per week for each model on the right-hand graph. Is there any relationship between decay and pollution? Write a hypothesis to explain any relationship you find between decay and pollution.

_____

_____

_____

Indicators of Decomposition

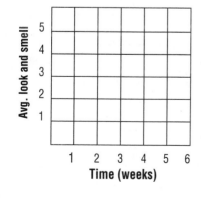

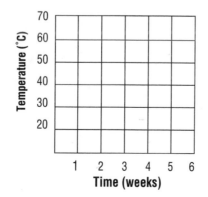

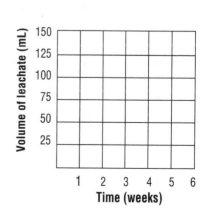

ANALYZE YOUR RESULTS

15. Compare the decay observed in the two types of landfills. What factors do you think encourage or limit decay?

_____

_____

_____

_____

16. Which kinds of garbage items decay most rapidly? most slowly? How might the slow-decaying items pose a long-term environmental threat?

_____

_____

_____

17. How can we reduce the environmental impact of slow-decaying items?

_____

_____

18. Which type of landfill will probably produce less leachate in the short run? in the long run? Explain your answer.

_____

_____

_____

_____

_____

_____

_____

_____

INVESTIGATION 12.2

PUTTING ECO-FRIENDLY CLEANSERS TO THE TEST

Supermarket shelves are crammed with products that make our lives easier. Oven cleaners, countertop sprays, toilet-bowl disinfectants, window-cleaning solvents, and countless other household products save us precious time and energy by doing their jobs quickly and with a minimum of effort. Chemicals in the spray-on, wipe-off oven cleaner quickly dissolve the grease and other muck that coats dirty ovens. The bleach you pour in your toilet contains chemicals that kill bacteria and break down chemical stains. But although these products may work well for their intended purposes, their ingredients can be hazardous. If you use these products without strictly following their safety guidelines, you may be endangering your health. And when you throw these products away, you may be releasing hazardous chemicals into the environment.

You might be surprised to discover how many commercial cleansers contain hazardous ingredients. In this investigation, you will survey several commercial products and record information about their hazardous properties. Then, you will make less hazardous, alternative products and test their effectiveness.

BACKGROUND

Cleansers work because a chemical reaction takes place between unwanted matter, mostly dirt and oil, and a cleaning agent. Most cleansers are surface-active chemicals, or *surfactants,* that remove dirt without destroying or damaging the surface to which the dirt is attached. Many cleansers are soaps with additives. Soap cleans because of its molecular properties; one part of a soap molecule is attracted to water while the other is attracted to oil, grease, or fat. The soap molecules surround the oily matter, which can then be rinsed away. Many things can be added to soap to help it work more effectively:

- Mechanical force, such as stirring or scrubbing, helps remove oily dirt.

- An abrasive cleanser combines a powdered abrasive, such as silica or pumice, with soap. An abrasive increases the friction, which removes oil and dirt from the surface more effectively.

Acid-base reactions are also common in household cleansers. For example, metal polishers use a strong acid or base to dissolve rust. Spot and stain removers also rely on the reactivity of strong acids or bases. Other cleaning products work by absorbing unwanted material.

MATERIALS

- soiled household items to be cleaned
- toilet-bowl cleaner
- laundry detergent
- bleach
- oven cleaner
- laundry stain remover
- drain opener
- window cleaner
- furniture polish
- all-purpose cleaner
- ingredients for eco-friendly cleansers: white vinegar, lemon juice, cut lemon, baking soda, washing soda, ammonia, chalk, borax, cream of tartar, olive oil
- mixing bowl
- spoon
- measuring cups
- measuring spoons
- spray bottle
- sponges
- nylon scouring pads
- steel wool
- paper towels
- newspaper

WHAT'S IN THE CUPBOARD?

1. Examine each of the following products: toilet-bowl cleaner, laundry detergent, bleach, oven cleaner, laundry stain remover, drain opener, window cleaner, and furniture polish. **Caution: Some chemicals may leak or there may be harmful residue on the containers.** On a sheet of paper, record the following data about each product:

   • name of product

   • presence of warning labels: CAUTION, WARNING, and/or DANGER

   • hazardous characteristics: toxic, flammable, explosive, caustic, and/or irritant

   • summary of precautions for using or disposing of the product

2. You are using a hazardous substance if the product label contains the words CAUTION, WARNING, or DANGER. Hazardous substances generally have at least one of the following labels:

   • *toxic:* poisonous, causing physical harm if inhaled, ingested, or absorbed; long-term effects may include cancer or birth defects

   • *flammable:* can catch fire or ignite easily

   • *explosive:* can explode if exposed to shock, heat, or pressure

   • *caustic:* corrosive, burning living tissue on contact

   • *irritant:* can cause skin, eye, or other irritations and inflammation on contact

3. After completing your survey, compare your data with that of other students. Which categories of products seem to be the most hazardous? Explain.

   _____

   _____

   _____

   _____

   _____

   _____

   _____

   _____

   _____

4. When you use hazardous products, it is important to take certain precautions to protect human health and the environment. Read the following safety guidelines, and write down why you think each one is important.

a. Leave hazardous products in their original containers.

_____

_____

_____

b. Keep hazardous products in well-ventilated areas, out of the reach of children or pets, and away from heat or sparks.

_____

_____

_____

c. Always use hazardous products in well-ventilated areas, and wear protective clothing if the product label tells you to.

_____

_____

_____

d. NEVER dispose of hazardous products by pouring them into storm drains or onto the ground.

_____

_____

_____

e. NEVER mix hazardous products together.

_____

_____

_____

TRY AN ALTERNATIVE

5. Select some common household objects that need cleaning. Prepare an appropriate, less-hazardous cleaning product according to the instructions in the table on the next page.

Recipes for Alternative Cleansers			
Drain opener	Pour 1 cup baking soda into drain, then add 1/2 cup warm white vinegar; cover drain for 1 min; rinse with cold water.	**Porcelain cleaner**	Rub on paste of borax and lemon juice; let sit for 2 hr; scrub with nylon scrubber and baking soda paste or cream of tartar paste.
Window cleaner	Mix 1/4 cup white vinegar in 1 qt water; spray on, and wipe with dry newspaper.	**Laundry stain remover**	To remove grease: rub chalk into the affected area, let sit for 15 min, then wash. To remove soil from whites: soak item in baking soda and water solution.
Oven cleaner	Fill spray bottle with equal parts ammonia and water; spray on, close door, and let set for 15 min; wipe off.	**Wood-furniture polish**	Mix 2 tbsp olive oil and 1 tbsp white vinegar, and slowly stir into 1 qt water. Apply to wood, and rub with cloth rag.

6. Test the alternative cleaning product on the soiled item. Continue to apply and use the product until the item is as clean as possible.

7. How effective was the alternative product?

_____

_____

8. What kinds of chemical reactions do you think took place when you used the alternative cleansers?

_____

_____

9. Do you think you have to use more or less mechanical force when using alternative cleansers than with commercial cleansers? Explain your answer.

_____

_____

_____

10. What are the advantages to using alternative cleansers instead of store-bought cleaning products?

_____

_____

_____

Name_____ Class_____ Date_____

I N V E S T I G A T I O N 13.1

WATCH A POPULATION GROW

What keeps our population from overrunning the Earth? You learned in Chapter 13 that populations increase exponentially until limiting factors reduce their growth rate. What are these limiting factors? Can they be overcome? In this Investigation, you will observe the growth of yeast in a closed system in order to better understand the factors that limit population growth.

MATERIALS

- molasses
- water
- 100 mL graduated cylinder
- stirring rod
- 100 mL beaker
- microscope
- microscope slides with coverslips
- capillary pipet (or eye-dropper)
- yeast solution

   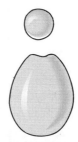

| A single yeast cell | A bud begins to form. | The bud grows. | The new bud breaks away from the original cell. |

When counting yeast cells, count the buds from asexual reproduction as well as the parent cells.

THE COUNTDOWN

1. Prepare a yeast culture medium by combining 45 mL of water and 5 mL of molasses in a 100 mL beaker. Stir the solution thoroughly.

2. Start a yeast culture by adding 10 drops of yeast solution to the culture medium.

3. Stir your yeast culture to evenly distribute the yeast cells; then immediately dip a capillary pipette into the beaker to collect a small quantity of yeast culture. Place one or two generous drops of yeast culture in the center of a microscope slide.

4. Gently cover the yeast culture with a coverslip.

5. Position the slide on your microscope. Use low power for focusing on the cells, and then switch to high power. Keep the light source dim so that you can see the cells more easily.

6. Count the number of yeast cells visible in the microscope's field of view under high power. Record the number of cells in the table below. Move the slide slightly, and repeat the count. Repeat two more times, recording your results in the table each time.

7. Calculate the average of your four cell counts. Calculate the average for the entire class. Record these averages in the table on the next page.

Yeast Cell Count						
Day	Observation 1	Observation 2	Observation 3	Observation 4	Average of 4 observations	Class average
0						
1						
2						
3						
4						
5						
6						
7						
8						
9						
10						

8. Repeat steps 3–7 each day for 10 days. Record your results in the table above. If a weekend or holiday prevents you from observing your culture for a day or two, indicate days when cell counts were unavailable.

   If the cells are too numerous to count, dilute a sample of the culture by combining 20 drops (about 1 mL) of culture with 9 mL of water in a test tube prior to counting. Multiply your cell count by 10 before recording it. If the population is still too dense, dilute further by combining 20 drops of the diluted culture with another 9 mL of water, and then multiply the count by 100.

9. Make a line graph showing the growth of your yeast population over time. Also graph the class-average values. In your graphs, remember to show a gap for any days when cultures were not observed.

EXPLOSIVE RESULTS?

10. How did the yeast population change over the course of 10 days? Why do you think this happened?

   _____

   _____

   _____

   _____

11. What factors could limit a population in nature?

_____

_____

_____

_____

_____

_____

_____

_____

12. Is the human population controlled by the same limiting factors that you listed above? Why or why not?

_____

_____

_____

_____

_____

_____

_____

_____

_____

PUSHING THE LIMITS

13. How do you think increasing the food supply of the yeast would affect the population curve? Write a hypothesis below.

_____

_____

_____

_____

_____

_____

14. Design an experiment to test the effect of increasing the food supply of the yeast. Write out your procedure below, being sure to explain how you will control all variables other than food supply.

_____

_____

_____

_____

_____

_____

_____

_____

_____

_____

15. After your teacher has approved your experimental design, carry out your experiment. Record and graph your data on a separate sheet of paper.

16. How did your yeast population graph differ when you increased the food supply? Was your hypothesis supported?

_____

_____

_____

_____

17. Why is increasing food production only a temporary solution to the human overpopulation problem?

_____

_____

_____

_____

I N V E S T I G A T I O N

13.2

POPPING POPULATIONS

The growth of natural populations is usually limited by resources, such as food and water, and by predators. However, when populations are not limited, they can grow surprisingly quickly. This is because each successive generation is larger than the last, yet each generation reproduces in the same amount of time.

Although all organisms are capable of exponential growth, it is usually only possible to observe rapid population growth in organisms that are small enough to find sufficient space and nutrients. For example, we can observe the exponential growth of a population of bacteria by putting a few bacteria in a large flask containing a nutrient-rich broth. The bacteria's population will increase exponentially, and the broth will become cloudy with bacteria in just a few days. A graph of this population's growth rate is shaped like a "J." Eventually, the bacteria will exhaust the limited space and nutrients. Once this happens, the population will "crash."

In this activity, you will simulate the exponential growth of a population. First, you will use a popcorn popper to "grow" a population of popcorn. Then you will use a computer to model and graph population growth.

MATERIALS

- popcorn kernels
- air popper
- air popper measuring cup
- 15 bowls
- stopwatch or watch that measures seconds
- graph paper
- IBM®-compatible computer or graphing calculator

CREATE A POPCORN POPULATION

1. Fill the air popper measuring cup to the top with popcorn. Level off the kernels with your hand.

2. STOP! Before you continue, read steps 3–7. Once the popcorn begins to pop, you will need to be prepared and ready to collect data.

3. Turn on the popper and pour in the popcorn kernels. The air popper may work better if it runs for 2–3 minutes before the popcorn is added. Place a bowl under the spout of the air popper to catch the popcorn.

4. As soon as the first popped kernel falls into the bowl, start the stopwatch, remove the bowl, and replace the bowl with an empty one. Every 15 seconds, remove the bowl under the popper spout and put another bowl under the spout. Keep track of the order in which the bowls are removed.

5. Continue to collect and set aside the popcorn every 15 seconds until all of the popcorn is popped. Turn off the popper.

INVESTIGATION 13.2, CONTINUED

6. Determine the population by counting the number of the kernels in each bowl. Record the data in the table below.

Popcorn Population Growth					
Time (seconds)	Bowl number	Number of kernels	Time (seconds)	Bowl number	Number of kernels
15	1		135	9	
30	2		150	10	
45	3		165	11	
60	4		180	12	
75	5		195	13	
90	6		210	14	
105	7		225	15	
120	8				

7. Describe the population growth recorded in the chart. What forces would allow for this kind of growth in a population of organisms?

_____

_____

_____

_____

8. On the next page, graph the relationship between elapsed time and population using your results. Plot each generation with the time popped on the horizontal (*x*) axis and the number of kernels per bowl on the vertical (*y*) axis. Draw a line connecting the points. Describe the shape of the line. What does this tell you about the population growth?

_____

_____

_____

_____

_____

INVESTIGATION 13.2, CONTINUED

Popcorn Population Growth Rate

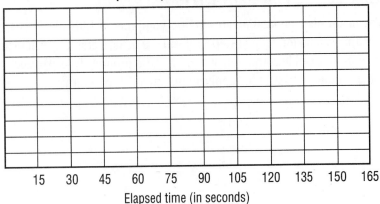

15 30 45 60 75 90 105 120 135 150 165

Elapsed time (in seconds)

ANALYZE YOUR RESULTS

9. Describe what happened to your population at progressive time intervals.

_____

_____

10. Does popping popcorn realistically model an exponentially growing population? Explain your answer.

_____

_____

_____

_____

_____

_____

11. Assume that fresh popcorn kernels pop much more readily than stale kernels. Would stale kernels be useful for simulating nonexponential growth? Why?

_____

_____

_____

MAKE A COMPUTER SIMULATION

12. We can simulate population growth on a computer or with a few keystrokes on a graphing calculator. Skip to step 15 if you are using a graphing calculator. With an IBM-compatible computer, start at the DOS prompt. Type "QBasic" and press <enter> to start the application. Enter this program:

```
x = 1
CLS
BEGIN:
CLS
x = x + 1
y = 2^ x
FOR n = 1 to y
PRINT "x";
NEXT n
INPUT m
GOTO BEGIN
```

13. The Xs on the screen represent organisms. Does this program realistically model exponential population growth? Explain your answer.

_____

_____

14. Use the following program to generate the number of organisms in each generation of an exponentially growing population.

```
x = 1
CLS
BEGIN:
x = x + 1
y = 2^ x
PRINT y
INPUT m
GOTO BEGIN
```

15. Next plot the growth of your simulated population on graph paper or on a graphing calculator. If you use a graphing calculator, generate the graph by entering: 2×2^x or $2(2^x)$ into the calculator. What happens to the population in each successive generation?

_____

_____

16. Compare the graphs of the popcorn population and the virtual population.

_____

_____

I N V E S T I G A T I O N 13.3

SO MANY PEOPLE!

In the last few decades the human population has doubled. In the decades ahead it will double again. The human population has grown so quickly that many fear we are at a crisis point. Indeed, many environmental problems occur simply because there are so many people.

The human population is growing unevenly throughout the world. In many developed countries, the population is growing very slowly or even declining. But in the less-developed parts of the world the population is growing at a significant rate. In a few countries, particularly the very poorest, the population is growing quite rapidly.

In this Investigation you will use census data to determine the growth rate of your community. Using this growth rate, you will estimate the growth of your community over the next few decades. Then, you will compute the population growth of your community using several hypothetical growth rates. Finally, you will project the future populations of the United States and the world based on their actual current growth rates.

MATERIALS

- almanac (containing census data) or statistical census abstract
- calculator (scientific model)

PROCEDURE

1. Use reference sources to determine the population of your community (or one nearby) in two recent successive years. Use the two most recent years available. If references do not contain this information or are unavailable, you can probably obtain the information from your Chamber of Commerce or city hall.

2. Use the population data to determine the growth rate of your community. The procedure for doing this is shown in the box on the next page.

3. Record your population information.

   a. population in the first year? _____

   b. population the following year? _____

   c. growth rate in percent? _____

4. Based on this growth rate, what will the population be 5 years from the first year for which you obtained census data? _____

   10 years? _____ 20 years? _____ 50 years? _____ 100 years? _____

5. Are each of the population projections you calculated in step 4 likely to be equally accurate? Why or why not?

   _____

   _____

   _____

Sample problem

2011 population: 100,000

2012 population: 104,000

Find the growth rate, and then use this growth rate to calculate the population 5 years from the year 2012.

Solution

Growth rate = second year population ÷ first year population

Growth rate = 104,000 ÷ 100,000 = 1.04

To change the growth rate to a percentage, subtract 1 then multiply by 100.

1.04 − 1 = 0.04; 0.04 × 100 = 4

Growth rate in percent = 4%

The following formula allows you to compute growth over multiple years.

Final population = initial population × (growth rate)^y,
where y is the number of years over which growth takes place.

You will need a calculator that can compute exponents to use this formula. Most scientific calculators are capable of this. If you do not have such a calculator, you will have to multiply the growth rate by itself for each year of growth.

Population in 2017 = 104,000 × (1.04)^5 = 126,532.

(Round to the nearest whole number.)

---

6. Calculate your city's growth over the next 100 years using the following hypothetical annual growth rates: 0.25 percent, 2 percent, and 4 percent. Graph your results in the space provided on the following page. Compute the data for 10 year intervals. Finish your calculations before you fill in the graph. But before you start calculating, make a prediction about the rate at which population will increase for each growth rate. For example, you might say "The population will increase twice as fast with a 4 percent growth rate as with a 2 percent growth rate" or "The population will double in 25 years with a 4 percent growth rate."

   What is your prediction? _____

   _____

   _____

7. In recent years, the population of the United States has increased by about 1 percent per year. Assuming a present population of 275 million and a constant growth rate, what will the population be in the year 2010? _____

   2020? _____ 2050? _____ 2100? _____

Population Growth

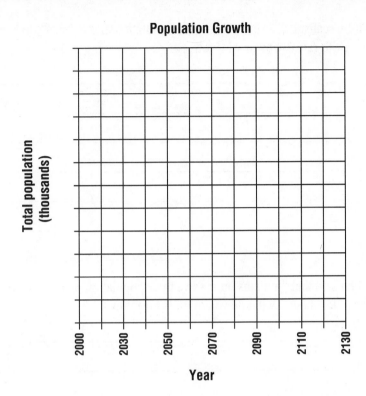

Year

8. The world's population is increasing by about 1.8 percent per year. Assuming a current population of 5.9 billion and a constant growth rate, what will the population be in 2050? _____ 2100? _____

THINK ABOUT IT

9. What kind of problems, if any, is your community likely to experience if its current rate of growth continues indefinitely? Explain.

_____

_____

_____

_____

_____

_____

_____

_____

_____

10. Would it be realistic to project the world population in the year 2300 based on today's growth rates? Why or why not?

_____

_____

_____

_____

_____

_____

_____

11. It has been said that "humans must solve their population problem or nature will solve it for them." What do you think is meant by this?

_____

_____

_____

_____

_____

_____

_____

_____

INVESTIGATION 13.4

PEBBLE MARK-RECAPTURE

One popular and simple technique for estimating a wild population of animals is called the *mark-recapture method.* It works like this: Suppose that you want to estimate the population of goldfish in a pond. You catch, tag, and release 40 fish. A few days later, you catch 40 fish and notice that 10 of the fish were tagged from the first catch—in other words, they were recaptured. To estimate the population of fish in the pond (N), multiply the number of fish in the first sample (M) by the number in the second sample (n), and divide the product by the number of "recaptures" (R).

$$\boxed{N = \frac{Mn}{R}} = \frac{\text{(first sample)} \times \text{(second sample)}}{\text{number recaptured}} = \text{estimated population}$$

To estimate the fish population,

$$\frac{40 \times 40 = 1600}{10} \quad \frac{1600}{10} = 160$$

Therefore, the estimated number of goldfish in the pond is 160. For the estimate to be accurate, you need to sample a fairly large population, and at least one animal must be captured in each sample. In general, the bigger your samples, the more accurate your estimate.

MATERIALS
- 1 qt. jar
- pebbles
- 2 shades of colored nail polish

USE THE FORMULA

1. You are an entomologist (a scientist who studies insects) trying to determine the population of Japanese beetles in your backyard. Two weeks ago you captured, marked, and released 100 beetles. Yesterday, you caught 40 beetles; 20 were recaptured from the first sample. Estimate the Japanese beetle population in your backyard. Show your work.

_____

_____

STALK THE WILD PEBBLE

2. Fill the jar half-way with pebbles. These pebbles represent a population of wild animals. Do not count the pebbles.

3. Remove a handful of pebbles from the jar. The handful represents your first sample of animals. Count the pebbles, and write the total on the line below. Paint each pebble in your sample with a drop of nail polish. After the polish dries, return the pebbles to the jar and thoroughly mix them with the others.

_____

4. Remove another handful of pebbles from the jar, and record the total below.

_____

5. Count and record the number of pebbles that were "recaptured."

_____

6. Use the formula to estimate the number of pebbles in the jar. Write your estimation on the line below. The formula is as follows:

$$N = \frac{Mn}{R} = \frac{(\text{first sample}) \times (\text{second sample})}{\text{number recaptured}} = \text{estimated population}$$

_____

7. Repeat steps 2–6 with the same jar of pebbles but use a different color of nail polish. Record your data below.

Number in first sample = _____

Number in second sample = _____

Number recaptured = _____

Estimated population = _____

8. Count the total number of pebbles in the jar. Record the number below.

_____

9. Compare the actual number of pebbles with the estimates in steps 6 and 7.

_____

_____

10. Based on what you observed in this exercise, do you think that the mark-recapture method is a good way to estimate population? Explain your answer.

_____

_____

EVALUATE THE METHOD

11. Imagine two ponds, one large and one small. You catch, tag, and release 20 goldfish from each pond. The next day, you catch 20 goldfish from each pond and count 8 recaptures from the small pond and 2 from the large pond.

a. Estimate the population of goldfish in the small pond.

_____

b. Estimate the population of goldfish in the large pond.

_____

c. Why would a large pond tend to have fewer recaptures than a small pond?

_____

_____

_____

12. Which of the following examples do you think reflects the largest population? Which reflects the smallest? Explain your answer.
   a. large first sample, large second sample, large recapture
   b. large first sample, large second sample, small recapture
   c. small first sample, large second sample, large recapture
   d. small first sample, small second sample, large recapture

_____

_____

_____

_____

_____

_____

13. a. If you captured, marked, and released 5 turtles from a pond, and caught 10 unmarked turtles the next day, would you have enough information to estimate the population using the mark-recapture method?

_____

_____

b. If you captured and marked one turtle from a pond and captured the same turtle the next day, can you conclude that only one turtle lives in the pond? Explain your answer.

_____

_____

_____

_____

14. Imagine that you are studying birds that are flying south for the winter. How might their migration affect the results of a mark-recapture study? Can you accurately estimate the migrating bird population using the mark-recapture method? Explain your answer?

_____

_____

_____

_____

THE PRISONER'S DILEMMA

The most pressing environmental problems, such as the loss of biodiversity and stratospheric ozone, are international in nature. The solution to these problems does not lie with one group or nation. Instead it ultimately depends on cooperation—between people, between businesses, and between governments. However, there are often advantages to not cooperating, or cheating, if you can get away with it. For example, once several nations agree to each reduce pollution by adopting expensive but environmentally friendly production methods, cheating becomes very attractive. By ignoring the expensive restrictions, a country can make more products for less money, so businesses stay profitable and citizens stay employed. It may be wrong to cheat on environmental agreements, but the financial and political incentives to do so are there.

In this activity, you will explore cooperation by playing a game. The game is derived from a story problem called "The Prisoner's Dilemma." Here is the story: Two suspects are arrested and placed in separate cells, where they cannot communicate with one another. The police urge each suspect to confess, but the suspects know that without a confession the police have a weak case. Of course each suspect hopes to go free. Knowing this, the police devise a plan. If one suspect confesses and provides evidence against the other, that suspect will go free and the other will get a harsh sentence. If both suspects confess, the police will give both suspects a moderate sentence because although they are guilty they were also honest. If neither suspect confesses, both suspects will receive a light sentence because the police lack evidence for a strong case. Each suspect must guess what the other suspect will do and act accordingly. Parties to an environmental agreement are faced with the same dilemma as these suspects are—to cheat or not to cheat?

CONSIDER THE DILEMMA

1. What do you think each suspect should do? What do you think each suspect will do? Explain your answer.

_____

_____

_____

_____

AN ENVIRONMENTAL "PRISONER'S DILEMMA"

Imagine that you make your living fishing in an area of the sea that lies within international waters. Because of overfishing, the population of fish in the area has drastically declined in recent years. In the past you were able to keep as much as you caught, sometimes up to 300 fish a day. Fishing is now regulated by an international agreement that prohibits anyone from catching more than 100 fish per day. This will give the population a chance to regenerate.

In order to be allowed to continue fishing, you have agreed to abide by this limit. The other people fishing in this area have agreed to this limit as well. There are now penalties for overfishing, but the chances of getting caught are slight. It is tempting to cheat on the agreement by catching more fish in order to make a better living. If you do cheat, you will probably not have any problems at first, but the other people fishing in your area may have a smaller catch as a result of your overfishing.

2. There are obvious benefits to cheating on this agreement. But are the long-term consequences worth it?

_____

_____

_____

_____

3. Assume that you have agreed to cooperate with a partner on resolving this environmental problem. Why should both parties agree to cooperate?

_____

_____

_____

4. What things are necessary for any international environmental agreement to be successful?

_____

_____

_____

_____

PLAY THE GAME

5. Play a game modeled on this environmental problem. Divide into pairs. Without consulting the other player, choose whether to cooperate (abide by the fishing agreement) or to cheat. Write your decision ("cooperate" or "cheat") on a slip of paper. Compare your answer with what your partner has decided.

6. Each player begins the game with 10 points. Score each round of play in the following manner. Record your score in the table below.

- If both players choose to cooperate, each earns 1 point.

- If both players cheat, they each lose 2 points.

- If one player cooperates and one cheats, the cheater earns 5 points while the cooperative player loses 3 points.

Environmental Dilemma: Scoring Chart				
	Player 1		Player 2	
	Cheat	Cooperate	Cheat	Cooperate
Round 1				
Round 2				
Round 3				
Round 4				
Round 5				
Round 6				
Round 7				
Round 8				
Total Score				

7. How many times did cheating happen in this game for your group?

_____

8. Now adjust your score according to your teacher's instructions. How many points did you end with in the game?

_____

9. Although both parties stand to benefit if each party cooperates on the agreement, cheating provides an opportunity for individual gain at a cost to the other party. Well-timed cheating builds your point count much faster than cooperation alone. Cheating, however, invites retaliation, which then lowers both players' scores.

Did you use a strategy when you played the game? If so, what was your strategy, and did it depend on what your opponent did?

_____

_____

_____

_____

10. Is this game a realistic model of the possible difficulties involved in enforcing international environmental treaties? Explain your answer.

_____

_____

11. How might the game be modified to prevent cheating or make it less attractive? Are there any ways these modifications could be applied to international agreements in the real world?

_____

_____

12. Not all agreements are bilateral (between just two sides). How might you modify the rules of the game to allow for three or more participants (multilateral agreements)? What might you need to change? Remember, the game should still be a good model; similar actions in the game and in the real world have similar rewards and risks.

_____

_____

_____

_____

TEXT INVESTIGATION 1

AN ONION CONUNDRUM

1. Scientific Problem: _____

_____

2. Variables: _____

_____

Hypothesis: _____

_____

4. How much of each substance will you use? _____

_____

What will your sample size be? _____

_____

Is it necessary to set up a control? Why or why not? _____

_____

Make a complete list of your procedures on a separate sheet of paper.

6. Record your data in the table. If you use more than three test tubes, make a table on a separate sheet of paper to record additional data. Make a line graph of the data in the space on the next page.

	Length of Roots (cm)		
Day	**Solution A: _____**	**Solution B: _____**	**Solution C: _____**
1			
2			
3			
4			
5			

TEXT INVESTIGATION, CONTINUED

Onion Growth in Test Solutions

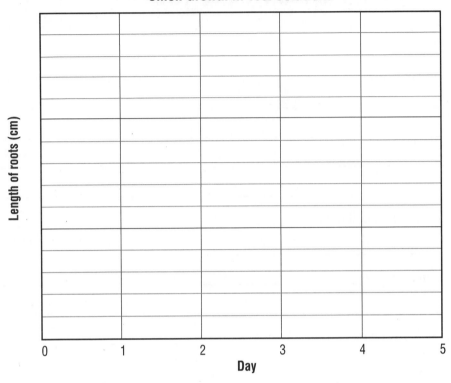

7. Write your report on a separate sheet of paper.

8. Variable changed: _____

_____

Variables held constant: _____

_____

Why is it important to change only one variable? _____

_____

_____

_____

9. Describe an experiment you could do to test the effect of another variable on plant growth.

_____

_____

_____

_____

_____

_____

T E X T   I N V E S T I G A T I O N   2

SHOWDOWN ON THE PRAIRIE

2. What is the purpose of the control pots? _____

_____

_____

3. Hypothesis: _____

_____

_____

5. Record your data in the table. Use a separate sheet of paper for more data if needed.

| | Species A Alone | | Species B Alone | | Plants in Mixed Pot | | | |
| | | | | | Species A | | Species B | |
	Max. height	No. of leaves	Max. height	No. of leaves	Max. height	No. of leaves	Max. height	No. of leaves
Day 1								
Day 2								
Day 3								
Day 4								
Day 5								
Day 6								
Day 7								

6. Graph your data on a separate sheet of paper.

7. How did the growth of each species in the absence of competition differ from its growth in the presence of competition?

_____

_____

_____

Did the experiment support your hypothesis? _____

_____

8. Why is it difficult to simulate competition in the laboratory? _____

_____

_____

9. Factor to investigate: _____

_____

10. Hypothesis: _____

_____

11. Record your experimental design on a separate sheet of paper.

12. Prediction: _____

_____

_____

13. On a separate sheet of paper, record your results in a data table.

14. Graph the results of your experiment on a separate sheet of paper.

15. Which grass species "won" in your classmates' competition experiments? _____

_____

Why might one species outcompete another? _____

_____

_____

_____

16. It is hard to draw conclusions about plant competition based on laboratory experiments because

_____

_____

_____

Possible additional experiments: _____

_____

_____

_____

_____

T E X T   I N V E S T I G A T I O N

WHAT'S IN AN ECOSYSTEM?

5. Kinds of plants and animals observed: _____

_____

_____

_____

_____

_____

_____

6. Producers: _____

Consumers: _____

Decomposers: _____

7. Organisms interacting with each other: _____

_____

_____

Organisms interacting with environment: _____

_____

_____

10. Food chains:

    (1) _____

    (2) _____

11. Do you expect to find more producers or more consumers? _____

Is this what you observed? _____

_____

_____

Explain your observations. _____

_____

_____

12. Decomposers observed: _____

Additional decomposers that might be present: _____

_____

13. What role do decomposers play? _____

_____

_____

What would happen if there were no decomposers? _____

_____

_____

_____

14. How are biotic factors affected by abiotic factors? _____

_____

_____

_____

How are abiotic factors affected by biotic factors? _____

_____

_____

_____

15. Question about the ecosystem: _____

_____

_____

An experiment or field study to investigate the question: _____

_____

_____

_____

_____

_____

Name_____ Class_____ Date_____

IDENTIFY YOUR LOCAL BIOME

1. Latitude: _____

2. Topography: _____

3. Record precipitation and temperature values in the table. Draw your climatogram below.

	Jan.	Feb.	Mar.	Apr.	May	June	July	Aug.	Sept.	Oct.	Nov.	Dec.
Precip. (cm)												
Temp. (°C)												

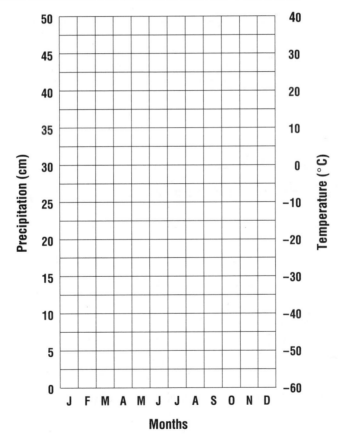

4. Record observations and sketches of plants on a separate sheet of paper.

5. Record observations and sketches of animals on a separate sheet of paper.

6. Biome with most similar climatogram: _____

7. Biome that best matches (considering all factors): _____

8. How plant adaptations meet conditions of biome:

(1) _____

_____

(2) _____

_____

(3) _____

_____

9. How animal adaptations meet conditions of biome:

(1) _____

_____

(2) _____

_____

(3) _____

_____

10. Does your climatogram match exactly? _____

How might these differences affect plant and animal adaptations? _____

_____

_____

_____

Could you notice any of those influences? _____

_____

_____

11. What features of your biome are created by the organisms that live there?

_____

_____

_____

Name _____ Class _____ Date _____

HOW SAFE IS OUR GROUNDWATER?

3. Record your observations in the table.

Observations of Substances in Surface Water		
Contaminant	**Appearance**	**Measurements (if any)**
Glucose (5 mL)		
Soil (5 mL)		
Food coloring (5 drops)		
Water (control)		

5. Predict how well the filters will clean each water sample.

glucose: _____

soil: _____

food coloring: _____

7. Record your observations of the filtered solutions in the table.

Observations of Substances in Groundwater		
Contaminant	**Appearance**	**Measurements (if any)**
Glucose		
Soil		
Food coloring		
Water (control)		

8. Is glucose still present? _____

Can you see it? _____

9. Was soil removed? How do you know? _____

Was food coloring removed? How do you know? _____

10. How accurate were your predictions? _____

_____

Conclusions: _____

_____

_____

11. Substance to test: _____

Prediction: _____

_____

Reasons for prediction: _____

_____

12. Observations of test solution before filtering: _____

_____

_____

Observations of test solution after filtering: _____

_____

_____

How did your results compare with your prediction? _____

_____

_____

13. Conclusions about what types of substances will or will not be filtered out by the earth: _____

_____

_____

_____

What precautions do you recommend for keeping groundwater clean? _____

_____

_____

_____

T E X T   I N V E S T I G A T I O N   6

HOW DOES ACID
PRECIPITATION AFFECT PLANTS?

4., 6., 9. Record your observations in the table.

Solution	Appearance of seeds after soaking	Total number of seeds	Number of seeds that germinated	Percentage of seeds that germinated
Water pH = _____				
Acid precipitation pH = _____				

10. What was the effect of "acid precipitation" on the seeds? _____

_____

If a farmer planted 10,000 seeds in soil that had been exposed to acid precipitation, how many plants would he lose?

_____

11. Hypothesis: _____

_____

12. Record your experimental procedure on a separate sheet of paper.

13. Prediction: _____

_____

14. Record your results in the table. Use a separate sheet of paper for additional data if needed.

Solution	Appearance of seeds after soaking	Total number of seeds	Number of seeds that germinated	Percentage of seeds that germinated

TEXT INVESTIGATION, CONTINUED

Solution	Appearance of seeds after soaking	Total number of seeds	Number of seeds that germinated	Percentage of seeds that germinated

15. Did your results agree with your prediction? _____

_____

Was your hypothesis supported? _____

_____

16. How did your experiment mimic real-world effects? _____

_____

_____

_____

How was it different from the real world? _____

_____

_____

_____

_____

How could you make your experiment more realistic? _____

_____

_____

_____

TEXT INVESTIGATION

GLOBAL WARMING IN A JAR

5. Record your data in the table. Use a separate sheet of paper for additional data if needed.

Time	Temperature	
	Uncovered jar (control)	Covered jar ("greenhouse")
Before going outdoors		
When first placed in sun		
+ 2 minutes		
+ 4 minutes		
+ 6 minutes		
+ 8 minutes		
+ 10 minutes		

6. Graph your results in the space below.

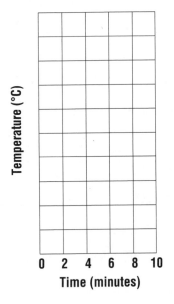

7. Hypothesis: _____

_____

8. Record your experimental design on a separate sheet of paper.

9. Prediction: _____

_____

11. Record your data in the table. Use a separate sheet of paper for additional data if needed.

Time	Temperature	
	Jar 1: _____	Jar 2: _____
Before going outdoors		
When first placed in sun		
+ 2 minutes		
+ 4 minutes		
+ 6 minutes		
+ 8 minutes		
+ 10 minutes		

12. Graph your results on a separate piece of paper.

13. Did your results agree with your predictions? _____

_____

What can you conclude? _____

_____

14. Which variables had the greatest influence? _____

_____

_____

Which had the least influence? _____

_____

15. How did your experiment model differences in global warming rates? _____

_____

_____

How did your model differ from the real world? _____

_____

_____

_____

T E X T   I N V E S T I G A T I O N

MINING FOR PEANUTS

2. Number of peanuts deposited: _____

In the space below, make a sketch of how the peanuts were distributed.

6. In the space below, sketch your completed landscape.

TEXT INVESTIGATION, CONTINUED

9. Number of peanuts you extracted: _____

10. How badly was the land damaged? _____

_____

How many peanuts were unearthed? _____

How many were buried? _____

How did number and distribution of peanuts affect mining results? _____

_____

How much waste was produced? _____

_____

Other observations: _____

_____

12. How hard was it to restore the site? _____

_____

How closely does the reclaimed site resemble the original site? _____

_____

13. How does this simulation compare to actual mining operations? _____

_____

_____

_____

14. How expensive do you think reclamation activities are compared with extracting the ore? _____

_____

15. Did all the mining companies recover the same amount of minerals? _____

If not, what accounted for the differences? _____

_____

_____

16. What guidelines would you give to new miners to reduce environmental harm? _____

_____

_____

T E X T   I N V E S T I G A T I O N

THE CASE OF
THE FAILING FARM

5. What happens as water is sprayed onto the land? _____

_____

6. Why are the streams becoming wider and shallower? _____

_____

_____

7. What is the effect of the "cow tracks"? _____

_____

_____

8. What happens if you cut the alfalfa? _____

_____

_____

9. Record the effect of the following modifications. If necessary, use a separate sheet of paper to describe the modification in more detail.

Planting corn and potato rows in different directions: _____

_____

_____

Exchanging alfalfa and corn crop locations: _____

_____

_____

Adding materials to soil: _____

_____

_____

Placing carpet in stream bed: _____

_____

_____

TEXT INVESTIGATION, CONTINUED

10. Note the effects of three other ideas for slowing erosion.

Idea 1: _____

_____

Effect: _____

_____

Idea 2: _____

_____

Effect: _____

_____

Idea 3: _____

_____

Effect: _____

_____

11. List five suggestions for preventing erosion on the Katawa farm.

(1) _____

_____

(2) _____

_____

(3) _____

_____

(4) _____

_____

(5) _____

_____

TEXT INVESTIGATION 10

BACKYARD DIVERSITY

3. Record features of your sites in Table A.

Table A		
Feature	**Site 1**	**Site 2**
Maintenance		
Time left undisturbed		
Sunlight exposure		
Soil		
Rain		
Slope		
Water drainage		
Vegetation cover		

TEXT INVESTIGATION, CONTINUED

5. Record your observations in Table B.

Table B		
	Site 1	**Site 2**
Number of insects		
Number of insect types		
Additional observations		

7. Best guess about reasons for differences between sites: _____

_____

8. Hypothesis: _____

_____

9. Describe an experiment to test your hypothesis. _____

_____

_____

_____

_____

_____

_____

_____

_____

_____

_____

TEXT INVESTIGATION

SOLAR DESIGN

3. Record temperatures in the table.

Time	Start	5 min.	10 min.	15 min.	20 min.	25 min.	30 min.
Temperature (°C)							

4. Hypothesis: _____

_____

5. Describe or sketch your new model design below:

6. Record your results in the table.

Time	Start	5 min.	10 min.	15 min.	20 min.	25 min.	30 min.
Temperature (°C)							

TEXT INVESTIGATION, CONTINUED

7. Did your second model reach a higher temperature than your first model? _____

_____

How do you account for the difference? _____

_____

_____

_____

_____

8. How did more efficient designs differ from your design? _____

_____

_____

_____

_____

_____

_____

_____

How would you redesign your model? _____

_____

_____

_____

_____

_____

_____

_____

9. If a passive solar heating system adds $5,000 to home construction costs, costs $25 per year to maintain, and saves $2,475 per year in heating costs, how long will it take for the solar heating system to pay for itself?

_____

_____

TEXT INVESTIGATION

DOES FAST FOOD HAVE TO BE WASTEFUL?

3. Notes about how food is packaged:

Materials used: _____

_____

_____

Layers of packaging: _____

_____

_____

Utensils, condiments, and napkins: _____

_____

_____

Other observations: _____

_____

_____

4. Number of people depositing trash in 30 minutes: _____

Notes about what is thrown away: _____

_____

_____

5. Estimated number of customers per day:

_____ × 2 × _____ × _____ × 2 = _____
People at one trash can   Hours per day   Number of trash cans

Notes: _____

_____

6. Estimated waste per customer: _____

_____

Estimated total daily waste: _____

_____

7. Are recycling containers provided? _____

_____

Are they clearly labeled? _____

_____

Are customers following recycling instructions? _____

_____

8. Make notes for your report to Ms. Fairweather here, and then write your report on a separate sheet of paper.

General findings: _____

_____

_____

_____

_____

Ways to avoid producing waste: _____

_____

_____

_____

Ways to replace disposable items with reusable ones: _____

_____

_____

_____

Waste items that could be recycled or composted: _____

_____

_____

_____

Ways to replace nonrecyclable, noncompostable items: _____

_____

_____

_____

TEXT INVESTIGATION ⑬

WHAT CAUSES A
POPULATION EXPLOSION?

2. Make an age-structure histogram below.

Age-Structure Histogram for 1995

Age	Males	Females
75–79		
70–74		
65–69		
60–64		
55–59		
50–54		
45–49		
40–44		
35–39		
30–34		
25–29		
20–24		
15–19		
10–14		
5–9		
0–4		

5,000   0   5,000

Population

3.–6. Record the results of your calculations in the table on the next page.

7. Graph the total population below.

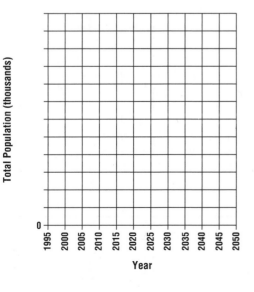

8. Make an age-structure histogram below.

Age-Structure Histogram for 2050

Age	Males	Females
75–79		
70–74		
65–69		
60–64		
55–59		
50–54		
45–49		
40–44		
35–39		
30–34		
25–29		
20–24		
15–19		
10–14		
5–9		
0–4		

0

Population

9. Which factor had a greater effect on population growth?

_____

_____

10. Did any of the graphs show no growth in population? Explain these results.

_____

_____

_____

_____

_____

_____

_____

_____

Age	1995	2000	2005	2010	2015	2020	2025	2030	2035	2040	2045	2050
75–79												
70–74												
65–69												
60–64												
55–59												
50–54												
45–49												
40–44												
35–39												
30–34												
25–29												
20–24												
15–19												
10–14												
5–9												
0–4												
Total												

Year

Name_____ Class_____ Date_____

14

BE AN ENVIRONMENTAL JOURNALIST

1. Make notes about relevant articles here, continuing on a separate sheet of paper as needed.

Article: _____

Summary: _____

_____

_____

Article: _____

Summary: _____

_____

_____

_____

Article: _____

Summary: _____

_____

_____

_____

Article: _____

Summary: _____

_____

_____

2. Issue chosen:_____

3. Copy the form on the next page to record information about each source you use.

How can the way that an issue is reported affect public opinion about it? _____

_____

4. Write your article on a separate sheet of paper.

5. How do your classmates' opinions compare with yours? _____

_____

RESEARCH SUMMARY FORM

Title: _____

Author: _____

Source: _____ Date: _____

Type of source: _____

Side(s) presented: _____

_____

Main points made: _____

_____

_____

_____

_____

_____

_____

_____

_____

Conflicting information: _____

_____

_____

Flaws in logic: _____

_____

_____

Biases: _____

_____

_____

Other notes: _____

_____

_____

_____